A Brief Introduction
to Theta Functions

Athena Series

SELECTED TOPICS IN MATHEMATICS

Edwin Hewitt, *Editor*

Richard Bellman

The Rand Corporation

A Brief Introduction
to Theta Functions

HOLT, RINEHART AND WINSTON

New York

To devotees
of analytic number theory

Foreword

The theory of elliptic functions is the fairyland of mathematics. The mathematician who once gazes upon this enchanting and wondrous domain crowded with the most beautiful relations and concepts is forever captivated.

Upon first browsing through this field, observing the numerous links to the theory of functions of a complex variable, to the theory of partial differential equations, to number theory, and even to statistical mechanics, one may be led to feel that it is wholly confined within the domain of analysis. A closer examination will show that the ties with algebra and topology are equally strong, and perhaps, on the most fundamental level, even stronger. Further observation shows that this theory, with its natural extensions—the theory of Abelian functions and modular functions—penetrates into virtually every area of mathematics and indeed requires all of these areas for its fruitful study.

In this short monograph, we wish to spotlight some of the high points of the fundamental regions and to indicate some of the powerful and versatile analytic methods that can be used to explore this field. Naturally, the choice has been highly subjective, involving results that appear to us to be of singular elegance. What is so magical about this theory is that relations that seem to be utterly unbelievable can be derived quite simply once the proper path is found. The many results from which to choose have all been of such grace and charm that it would be difficult indeed to produce any pedestrian combination.

We have tried consistently, we hope, to maintain an elementary level. By this, we mean that the text should be intelligible to an upper senior or first-year graduate student familiar with the rudiments of the theory of functions of a complex variable and with the usual manipulations of series and integrals by which the analyst earns his daily bread. Apart from a few classic theorems concerning the uniqueness of Laplace and Fourier transforms, the text is self-contained. These few results are of an intuitive nature that the student may accept on faith or find in standard books (which, of course, constitutes another form of acceptance on faith). A number of references are given to enable the interested reader to pursue any branch of the subject in depth.

I wish to express my gratitude to L. Mordell and S. Lehman who read the manuscript through and made a number of very helpful comments and suggestions, to express my thanks to P. Lax for some encouraging remarks, and to thank E. Hewitt and J. Lehner for much detailed and useful criticism.

R. B.

Santa Monica, California
April, 1961

Contents

*A Brief Introduction
to Theta Functions*

1. Introduction

Let us begin by introducing the functions whose many properties we shall study. Consider the function of z defined by the infinite series

$$f(z) = \sum_{n=-\infty}^{\infty} e^{-n^2 t + 2niz}. \tag{1.1}$$

Here z is a complex variable, permitted to assume any value, while t is a complex parameter satisfying the condition $Re(t) > 0$. It is easy to see that the series converges absolutely and uniformly in any bounded region of the z plane, and thus that $f(z)$ is an entire function of z. It is clear, furthermore, that $f(z)$ is periodic with period π,

$$f(z + \pi) = f(z). \tag{1.2}$$

Despite its rather special form, $f(z)$ is no artificially concocted function. On the contrary, it is one of the basic functions of analysis, a *theta function*. It occurs in a crucial role in the development of the theory of linear partial differential equations of parabolic type, in the study of the Riemann zeta function and in connection with the representation of numbers as sums of squares, thus occupying a major position in the analytic theory of numbers, and, in its most fundamental role, it is a keystone of the theory of elliptic functions.

Jacobi, in his magnum opus, *Fundamenta Nova . . .*, was the first mathematician to study these functions in a thorough fashion. True to the spirit of his time, a spirit compounded of equal parts of faith and nearly incredible ingenuity, he derived his many elegant and intricate results by means of the algebraic manipulations familiar to Euler and Gauss. Once exhibited, the results are readily verified by means of the theory of functions of a complex variable, using Liouville's theorem. Moreover, as we shall see, we now possess a number of powerful techniques for deriving results of this nature. Some are valid only for functions of one complex variable, while others can be used for functions of many variables.

Despite our unqualified title, our aim is not so ambitious as to present any complete, or even partially complete theory of theta functions. This domain is of such magnitude and extent that it cannot be mapped in any brief or simple fashion. Instead, we wish to use three principal results in the theory of elliptic functions, all expressible in terms of theta functions, as a stage upon which to parade some of the general factota of analysis, and as an excuse to discuss some intimately related results of great mathematical elegance. Our aim is to indicate the applicability and versatility of analytic techniques that should be part of the hope chest of every young mathematician.

Consequently, we shall neither follow the ingenious derivations of Jacobi—certainly one of the great mathematical tours de force—nor shall we slavishly follow the well traced path of the theory of functions of a complex variable. Both types of presentations are readily available, obviating any need for complete repetition here. We shall, however, use the spirit of these methods here and there.

Agreeing with the wry observation of Whittaker and Watson concerning the proliferation of notations, we have endeavored to make it as easy as possible for the reader by following the notation of these authors to a great extent.

Comments and References

For a detailed discussion of the theory of theta functions and the connection with elliptic functions, see

Whittaker, E. T., and Watson, G. N., *A Course of Modern Analysis*, 4th ed. Cambridge: Cambridge Univ. Press., 1935.

Many further references will be found therein.

2.   The Four Types of Theta Functions

Although it will soon be seen that we could restrict ourselves to the introduction of just one basic function, say the function defined in (1.1), it turns out to be very convenient to introduce *four* functions. Conforming to Whittaker and Watson, as stated above, we write

$$\theta_1(z, t) = 2q^{1/4} \sin z - 2q^{9/4} \sin 3z + 2q^{25/4} \sin 5z - \dots,$$
$$\theta_2(z, t) = 2q^{1/4} \cos z + 2q^{9/4} \cos 3z + 2q^{25/4} \cos 5z + \dots,$$
$$\theta_3(z, t) = 1 + 2q \cos 2z + 2q^4 \cos 4z + 2q^9 \cos 6z + \dots,$$
$$\theta_4(z, t) = 1 - 2q \cos 2z + 2q^4 \cos 4z - 2q^9 \cos 6z + \dots. \tag{2.1}$$

Here

$$q = e^{\pi i t}, \tag{2.2}$$

and $|q| < 1$ if and only if $Im(t) > 0$. We henceforth assume that this relation holds. All four of the series appearing above define entire periodic functions of z. These periodicity properties will be noted below.

When the precise value of q is of no import, we shall suppress the dependence upon q, and write more simply $\theta_1(z)$, $\theta_2(z)$, $\theta_3(z)$, and $\theta_4(z)$ for these four functions.

We leave to the reader the straightforward task of establishing the functional relationships

$$\theta_1(z) = - \theta_2\left(z + \frac{\pi}{2}\right) = - iM\theta_3\left(z + \frac{\pi}{2} + \frac{\pi t}{2}\right) = - iM\theta_4\left(z + \frac{\pi t}{2}\right),$$

$$\theta_2(z) = M\theta_3\left(z + \frac{\pi t}{2}\right) = M\theta_4\left(z + \frac{\pi}{2} + \frac{\pi t}{2}\right) = \theta_1\left(z + \frac{\pi}{2}\right),$$

$$\theta_3(z) = \theta_4\left(z + \frac{\pi}{2}\right) = M\theta_1\left(z + \frac{\pi}{2} + \frac{\pi t}{2}\right) = M\theta_2\left(z + \frac{\pi t}{2}\right),$$

$$\theta_4(z) = -iM\theta_1\left(z + \frac{\pi t}{2}\right) = iM\theta_2\left(z + \frac{\pi}{2} + \frac{\pi t}{2}\right) = \theta_3\left(z + \frac{\pi}{2}\right), \qquad (2.3)$$

where the multiplier M is given by

$$M = q^{1/4}e^{iz}. \qquad (2.4)$$

Comments and References

Were we to start the theory of elliptic functions from scratch it would be most sensible, as pointed out to me by L. J. Mordell, to use the notation of Weber, "Lehrbuch der Algebra," vol. 3. The functions $\theta_{gh}(z, w)$ are introduced, possessing the functional equations

$$\theta_{gh}(z + w, w) = (-1)^h e^{-2\pi i(2z+w)} \theta_{gh}(z, w),$$

$$\theta_{gh}(z + 1, w) = (-1)^g \theta_{gh}(z, w). \qquad (2.5)$$

The great advantage of this notation lies in the fact that the subscripts determine the functional equations, and make it quite easy to remember many important properties of the theta functions which are not at all evident in our notation.

3. Fundamental Domain

From the foregoing relations, or directly, we see that

$$\theta_1(z) = -\theta_1(z + \pi),$$

$$\theta_1(z) = -qe^{2iz}\theta_1(z + \pi t). \qquad (3.1)$$

These relations tell us that the function $\theta_1(z)$ is completely determined throughout the entire plane by the values it assumes in any parallelogram of the form of Figure 1.

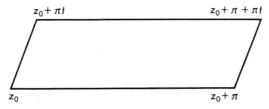

Fig. 1

This important fact will be used subsequently. The corresponding results for the other three theta functions are

$$\theta_2(z + \pi) = -\theta_2(z), \qquad \theta_2(z + \pi t) = q^{-1}e^{-2iz}\theta_2(z),$$
$$\theta_3(z + \pi) = \theta_3(z), \qquad \theta_3(z + \pi t) = q^{-1}e^{-2iz}\theta_3(z),$$
$$\theta_4(z + \pi) = \theta_4(z), \qquad \theta_4(z + \pi t) = -q^{-1}e^{-2iz}\theta_4(z). \qquad (3.2)$$

From these relations, we readily conclude that any parallelogram of the foregoing type is a fundamental domain for $\theta_2(z)$, $\theta_3(z)$, or $\theta_4(z)$.

4. First Basic Result

In addition to the foregoing functional equations which lie completely on the surface, the theta functions satisfy a host of recondite transformation formulas.

One of the most fascinating of these is the following:

Theorem 1:

$$\theta_3(z, t) = (-it)^{-1/2}e^{z^2/\pi it}\theta_3\left(\frac{z}{t}, -\frac{1}{t}\right). \qquad (4.1)$$

The square root is to be interpreted as the principal value; that is, if $w = re^{i\theta}$, where $0 \le \theta < 2\pi$, then $w^{1/2} = r^{1/2}e^{i\theta/2}$. Observe that in this relation both z and t undergo transformations.

Theorem 1, simply stated as it is, has amazing ramifications in the fields of algebra, number theory, geometry, and other parts of mathematics. In fact, it is not easy to find another identity of comparable significance. We shall make some effort in the coming pages to justify this apparently extravagant statement.

Comments and References

The general result was discussed by Poisson in 1827, while the particular result with $z = 0$ was discovered by him in 1823. A good deal of historical comment is given in the treatise of Whittaker and Watson cited above. See also

Dickson, L. E., *History of the Theory of Numbers*, vol. II. Washington, D. C.: Carnegie Institution, 1920.

5. Fourier Series

Since our first method of proof of theorem 1 will be based upon the theory of Fourier series, let us briefly digress to present the rudiments of this theory.

Consider the set of exponential functions $\{e^{2\pi inx}\}$, where n assumes the values $n = 0$, $n = \pm 1$, $n = \pm 2$, and so on. These are clearly periodic functions of x

of period one. It is plausible, from a number of physical considerations, to suspect that every continuous function of x which is periodic of period one can be represented as a linear combination of these particular functions. In other words, our physical surmise is that every periodic motion is a superposition of these simple periodic motions.

Setting

$$f(x) = \sum_{n=-\infty}^{\infty} a_n e^{2\pi i n x}, \tag{5.1}$$

how do we determine the coefficients? Fourier solved the problem by expanding both sides as power series in x and "solving" the resulting system of linear equations for the a_n. Following Euler, let us employ the orthogonality relation

$$\int_0^1 e^{2\pi i m x} e^{-2\pi i n x} \, dx = \delta_{mn}. \tag{5.2}$$

Here δ_{mn} is the Kronecker delta symbol defined by the relations $\delta_{mn} = 0$, $m \neq n$, $\delta_{mn} = 1$, $m = n$. It is reasonable then to suppose that if 5.1 holds, then the coefficient a_n is determined by the simple formula

$$a_n = \int_0^1 f(x) \, e^{-2\pi i n x} \, dx. \tag{5.3}$$

Oddly, despite the physical simplicity of the situation, its mathematical aspects are both extraordinarily complex and subtle. The difficulty is essentially that the physical, intuitive concept of a continuous function is far too naive for the mathematical definition of a continuous function. Consequently, we circumvent a number of irritating pitfalls by working backwards. We start with a continuous function $f(x)$, (a type of function sufficiently general for our subsequent purposes) and form the sequence of Fourier coefficients, $\{a_n\}$, $n = 0, \pm 1, \pm 2, \ldots$, by means of the formula 5.3. Using these coefficients, we form the series

$$g(x) = \sum_{n=-\infty}^{\infty} a_n e^{2\pi i n x} \tag{5.4}$$

where x is a real variable, lying in the open interval $[0,1]$. This series yields a new function $g(x)$, defined where 5.4 converges.

We then ask ourselves two questions:

(a) Does 5.4 converge for all x, and, if not, for what values of x does it converge?

(b) When 5.4 converges, is it equal to the function $f(x)$?

Question (a) remains unanswered up to the present day. Question (b) is answered in the affirmative. The series 5.4 converges to $f(x)$ if it converges at all. If we replace convergence in the usual sense by (C, 1) summability, then, following Fejer, we can obtain elegant and satisfying results. Fortunately, for the applications which we require, we can get by with very simple considerations.

Theorem 2: *If*

$$\sum_{n=-\infty}^{\infty} |a_n| < \infty, \tag{5.6}$$

the infinite series 5.4 converges uniformly (and of course absolutely) for all x in [0,1] to f(x).

Proof. It is clear that the convergence of the series in 5.6 implies the uniform and absolute convergence of the infinite series 5.4. Hence, we have

$$\int_0^1 g(x)\, e^{-2\pi i n x}\, dx = \int_0^1 \left(\sum_{k=-\infty}^{\infty} a_k e^{2\pi i k x} \right) e^{-2\pi i n x}\, dx$$

$$= \sum_{k=-\infty}^{\infty} a_k \int_0^1 e^{2\pi i k x} e^{-2\pi i n x}\, dx \tag{5.7}$$

(by virtue of uniform convergence)

$$= a_n.$$

From this, it follows that $f(x)$ and $g(x)$ are two continuous functions of x having the same Fourier coefficients; that is,

$$\int_0^1 [f(x) - g(x)]\, e^{2\pi i n x}\, dx = 0, \tag{5.8}$$

for $n = 0, \pm 1, \dots$.

It is now plausible that the function $f(x) - g(x)$ must be identically zero, and it is indeed true. Since this result can be established in a variety of ways, without further recourse to the theory of Fourier series, we shall accept it without furnishing any proof here. As usual, ingenuity is required if standard theory is not used. On the other hand, one of the basic results of the theory of Fourier series—the summability theorem of Fejer—yields the result immediately as a corollary of a far more general result.

Comments and References

The fundamental summability theorem of Fejer is given in

Fejér, L., *Math. Ann.*, **58** (1904) 51.

For an exhaustive treatment of the modern theory of Fourier series, see

Zygmund, A., *Trigonometric Series*, (2nd ed.), 2 vols. Cambridge: Cambridge Univ. Press, 1959.

For a quick view of some important results, see

Titchmarsh, E. C., *Theory of Functions*. Oxford: Oxford Univ. Press, 1937.

6. The Poisson Summation Formula

An important application of the theory of Fourier series is to Poisson's summation formula. This elegant and powerful technique can be used to derive a number of significant results in analysis.

Let $f(x)$ be a continuous function of x, defined for $-\infty < x < \infty$. Form the periodic function

$$g(x) = \sum_{n=-\infty}^{\infty} f(x+n). \tag{6.1}$$

For the moment, let us proceed quite formally, assuming that the series converges, that the manipulations that follow are valid, and so on. Subsequently, we shall present a rigorous treatment.

It is clear that

$$g(x) = g(x+1). \tag{6.2}$$

Let us now invoke a mathematical principle first explicitly enunciated, and systematically exploited, by Hecke: *A periodic function should always be expanded in a Fourier series.*

To obtain the Fourier coefficients of $g(x)$ we write

$$a_k = \int_0^1 g(x)\, e^{-2\pi i k x}\, dx = \int_0^1 \left[\sum_{n=-\infty}^{\infty} f(x+n) \right] e^{-2\pi i k x}\, dx$$

$$= \sum_{n=-\infty}^{\infty} \int_0^1 f(x+n)\, e^{-2\pi i k x}\, dx$$

$$= \sum_{n=-\infty}^{\infty} \int_n^{n+1} f(x)\, e^{-2\pi i k x}\, dx = \int_{-\infty}^{\infty} f(x)\, e^{-2\pi i k x}\, dx. \tag{6.3}$$

Consequently, provided we can justify all of the above, we have the identity

$$\sum_{n=-\infty}^{\infty} f(x+n) = \sum_{k=-\infty}^{\infty} e^{2\pi i k x} \int_{-\infty}^{\infty} f(x_1)\, e^{-2\pi i k x_1}\, dx_1. \tag{6.4}$$

The case $x = 0$ yields the *Poisson summation formula:*

$$\sum_{n=-\infty}^{\infty} f(n) = \sum_{k=-\infty}^{\infty} \int_{-\infty}^{\infty} f(x_1)\, e^{-2\pi i k x_1}\, dx_1. \tag{6.5}$$

Comments and References

For a historical survey of summation formulae, which go back to Euler, Plana and Abel, see the monograph

Lindelof, E., *Le Calcul des Residus et Ses Applications.* New York: Chelsea Publ. Co., 1947.

A number of very elegant applications will be found in this treatise.

The principle of Hecke is actually a particular case of a more embracing dictum to the effect that invariance under a group of transformations should always be made explicit, usually by means of an expansion in terms of group characters.

Let us note the following simple extension of 6.4 due to G. N. Watson:

$$\sum_{n=-\infty}^{\infty} g(n+s)\, e^{\pi i t(2n+s)} = \sum_{n=-\infty}^{\infty} f(n+t)\, e^{\pi i s(2n+t)},$$

where

$$g(x) = \int_{-\infty}^{\infty} f(y)\, e^{-2\pi i x y}\, dy.$$

7. Some Simple Sufficient Conditions

Examining the procedure of Section 6, we see that the imposition of some very simple conditions, which are easy to apply, will justify our procedures. Let us suppose that

(a) The function $f(x)$ is continuous for all real finite x;

(b) The infinite series,

$$\sum_{n=-\infty}^{\infty} f(x+n)$$

converges uniformly in every finite x interval;

(c) The infinite integral $\int_{-\infty}^{\infty} |f(x)|\, dx$ converges;

(d) The series

$$\sum_{k=-\infty}^{\infty} |a_k|,$$

converges, where a_k is the Fourier coefficient determined in 6.3.

Then:

Theorem 3: *Under the foregoing conditions, the two sides of 6.4 exist and are equal for all x.*

Comments and References

An enormous amount of effort has been devoted to the study of conditions under which the Poisson summation formula is valid. The simple conditions above, although exceedingly restrictive, are sufficient for our present purposes.

The reader interested in more precise results may refer to

Titchmarsh, E. C., *Theory of Functions.* Oxford: Oxford Univ. Press, 1939.
Mordell, L. J., "Poisson's summation formula and the Riemann zeta-function." *J. Lond. math. Soc.,* **4** (1928) 285-291.
Linfoot, E. H., "A sufficiency condition for Poisson's formula." *J. Lond. math. Soc.,* **4** (1928) 54.

8. An Infinite Integral

Having taken care of these essential preliminaries, we turn to the evaluation of an infinite integral, perhaps the most important infinite integral in analysis.

In order to apply the preceding summation formula to obtain the transformation formula for $\theta_3(z, t)$, we must evaluate the infinite integral

$$\int_{-\infty}^{\infty} e^{-tx^2+2\pi ikx} \, dx. \tag{8.1}$$

Let us consider then the general integral

$$h(y, t) = \int_{-\infty}^{\infty} e^{-tx^2+2xy} \, dx, \tag{8.2}$$

where t and y are complex quantities. The variable y may assume any value, while t must have a positive real part.

If t and y are real, the analytic form of $h(y, t)$ is easily ascertained. We have, making an obvious change of variable,

$$h(y, t) = \frac{1}{\sqrt{t}} \int_{-\infty}^{\infty} e^{-x^2+(2xy/\sqrt{t})} \, dx$$

$$= \frac{e^{y^2/t}}{\sqrt{t}} \int_{-\infty}^{\infty} e^{-[x-(y/\sqrt{t})]^2} \, dx$$

$$= \frac{e^{y^2/t}}{\sqrt{t}} \int_{-\infty}^{\infty} e^{-x^2} \, dx.$$

Hence,

$$h(y, t) = \frac{c e^{y^2/t}}{\sqrt{t}}, \tag{8.4}$$

where c is an as yet undetermined constant.

The simplest procedure to follow at this point is an appeal to analytic continuation. It is easy to show directly from the representation appearing in 8.2 that $h(y, t)$ is an entire function of y and an analytic function of t for $Re(t) > 0$. Hence, the representation of 8.4, established for real y and t, is valid for all y and all t, such that $Re(t) > 0$.

There are, of course, many special techniques which can be employed. Let us accept the fact that $h(y, t)$ has the stated form, and turn to the evaluation of the constant c.

Again there are many interesting methods at our disposal, the most direct of which relies upon the gamma function. We have

$$\int_{-\infty}^{\infty} e^{-x^2}\, dx = 2 \int_{0}^{\infty} e^{-x^2}\, dx = \int_{0}^{\infty} e^{-u} u^{-1/2}\, du = \Gamma\left(\frac{1}{2}\right) = \sqrt{\pi}. \qquad (8.5)$$

A completely elementary technique of some ingenuity is the following. We write

$$c^2 = \left(\int_{-\infty}^{\infty} e^{-x^2}\, dx\right)\left(\int_{-\infty}^{\infty} e^{-y^2}\, dy\right)$$

$$= \int_{-\infty}^{\infty}\int_{-\infty}^{\infty} e^{-(x^2+y^2)}\, dx\, dy, \qquad (8.6)$$

and convert to polar coordinates. The result is

$$c^2 = \int_{0}^{2\pi}\int_{0}^{\infty} e^{-r^2} r\, dr\, d\theta = 2\pi \int_{0}^{\infty} e^{-r^2} r\, dr = \pi. \qquad (8.7)$$

Hence, again, $c = \sqrt{\pi}$.

Putting the foregoing results together and replacing y by iy, we have the fundamental relation

$$\int_{-\infty}^{\infty} e^{-tx^2 + 2\pi ixy}\, dx = \sqrt{\frac{\pi}{t}}\, e^{y^2/t} \qquad (8.8)$$

for $Re(t) > 0$, and all y.

9.   The Transformation Formula for $\theta_3(z, t)$

It is easy to see that the function $f(x) = e^{-tx^2}$, $Re(t) > 0$, satisfies the conditions of theorem 3. Using the result of 8.8, and the identity of 6.4, we obtain the relation

$$\sum_{n=-\infty}^{\infty} e^{-t(x+n)^2} = \sum_{k=-\infty}^{\infty} e^{2\pi ikx} \int_{-\infty}^{\infty} e^{-tx_1^2 - 2\pi ikx_1}\, dx_1 \qquad (9.1)$$

$$= \sqrt{\frac{\pi}{t}} \sum_{k=-\infty}^{\infty} e^{2\pi ikx - (\pi^2 k^2/t)}.$$

We leave it to the reader to show that this is equivalent to the transformation formula for $\theta_3(z, t)$ stated in theorem 1. The case $x = 0$ yields the remarkable result

$$\sum_{n=-\infty}^{\infty} e^{-tn^2} = \sqrt{\frac{\pi}{t}} \sum_{n=-\infty}^{\infty} e^{-\pi^2 n^2/t}, \tag{9.2}$$

or

$$g(t) = \sum_{n=-\infty}^{\infty} e^{-n\pi^2 t} = \sqrt{\frac{1}{t}} \sum_{n=-\infty}^{\infty} e^{-\pi n^2/t} = \sqrt{\frac{1}{t}} g\left(\frac{1}{t}\right) \tag{9.3}$$

for $Re(t) > 0$.

10. Numerical Application

Results of the foregoing type are extremely important for the purposes of analytic and arithmetic approximation. As a matter of fact, one of the main functions of the Poisson summation formula is the systematic supplying of such approximations.

Suppose that we wish to evaluate the function

$$\sum_{n=-\infty}^{\infty} e^{-n^2 t}$$

at the point $t = 0.01$. Although the series clearly converges for $t > 0$, any direct attempt at summation for a small value of t such as this meets with considerable difficulty. For $t = 0.01$, we require fifty terms to reach a term of the magnitude of

$$e^{-25} = 10^{-25\log_{10}e} = 10^{-25(0.4343)} \simeq 10^{-10.8} \tag{10.1}$$

Consequently, use of the first fifty terms would yield an accuracy of the order of ten significant figures.

Consider, however, the right-hand side of 9.2. The *smaller* the value of t, the more accurate the approximation furnished by the first few terms. At $t = 0.01$, we have

$$\sum_{n=-\infty}^{\infty} e^{-n^2(0.01)} = \sqrt{\frac{\pi}{0.01}} \left(1 + 2e^{-100\pi^2} + ...\right). \tag{10.2}$$

Since $\pi^2 \simeq 9.89 \simeq 10$, we have

$$e^{-100\pi^2} \simeq e^{-1000} \simeq 10^{-1000(0.4343)} \simeq 10^{-434}. \tag{10.3}$$

Two terms of this series yield an accuracy of the order of four hundred significant figures: a phenomenally successful approximation!

It is the presence of the theta functions that makes elliptic functions a useful computational tool. Although the series defining the elliptic functions converge very slowly, their representations in terms of theta functions permit quick and accurate computation.

Comments and References

The theory of elliptic functions can be based upon either the Jacobi theta functions or the Weierstrassian elliptic functions. The former is most useful for numerical applications and for applications to analytic number theory; the latter for the foundations of the theory.

The Weierstrassian functions can be expressed in terms of the theta functions. A detailed discussion may be found in Whittaker and Watson.

11. Modular Functions and Eisenstein Series

Consider the function

$$\theta_3(0, t) = \phi(t) = \sum_{n=-\infty}^{\infty} e^{n^2 \pi i t}. \tag{11.1}$$

It is clear that $\phi(t)$ is periodic in t, with period 2,

$$\phi(t + 2) = \phi(t), \tag{11.2}$$

and the fundamental transformation formula tells us that

$$\phi(t) = \sqrt{\frac{\pi}{it}}\, \phi\left(-\frac{1}{t}\right). \tag{11.3}$$

We see then that there are two simple t transformations,

$$T_1(t) = t + 2,$$

$$T_2(t) = -\frac{1}{t}, \tag{11.4}$$

each a linear fractional transformation, which lead to simple transformations of $\phi(t)$. Combining them in various ways, we are led to still further functional relations. For example,

$$\phi(t) = \phi(t + 2) = \sqrt{\frac{\pi}{i(t + 2)}}\, \phi\left(-\frac{1}{t + 2}\right)$$

$$= \sqrt{\frac{\pi}{i(t + 2)}}\, \phi\left(-\frac{1}{t + 2} + k\right)$$

$$= \sqrt{\frac{\pi}{i(t + 2)}}\, \phi\left(\frac{kt + 2k - 1}{t + 2}\right). \tag{11.5}$$

Applying T_1 a certain number of times, then T_2, then T_1 another number of times, and so on, we obtain a relation of the form

$$\phi(t) = \frac{p(a,b,c,d)}{(ct+d)^{1/2}} \phi\left(\frac{at+b}{ct+d}\right), \qquad (11.6)$$

where a, b, c, and d are certain integers (allowing zero as a possible value), and $p(a,b,c,d)$ is a constant dependent, as indicated, upon the values a, b, c, and d.

It is easy to see that $ad - bc = 1$, since this property holds for the transformations T_1 and T_2.

Taking even powers, we can eliminate the irrationality. Thus,

$$\phi(t)^{2r} = \frac{p^{2r}}{(ct+d)^r} \phi\left(\frac{at+b}{ct+d}\right)^{2r}. \qquad (11.7)$$

This transformation formula allows us to obtain a very accurate evaluation of $\phi[(at+b)/(ct+d)]$ as $t \to 0$—which is to say, an extremely precise estimate for the behavior of $\phi(s)$ as $s \to b/d$. We shall discuss the application of this to analytic number theory below.

In this way, we are led to study a remarkable class of functions, $f(z)$, satisfying a functional equation

$$f(z) = \frac{k}{(cz+d)^r} f\left(\frac{az+b}{cz+d}\right) \qquad (11.8)$$

for $Im(z) > 0$, the automorphic functions of Poincaré-Fuchs-Klein. This is one of the most fascinating and difficult domains of analysis, which we shall not investigate here.

Consider, on an apparently different tack, the series

$$E_r(t) = \Sigma' \frac{1}{(mt+n)^{2r}}, \qquad (11.9)$$

(convergent for $r > 1$), where the prime indicates that the summation is over all integer values of m and n except for the pair $m = n = 0$. Assume that the complex variable t is to have a positive imaginary part, and that r is an integer greater than 2. Series of this type are called *Eisenstein series*.

Let

$$t = \frac{at'+b}{ct'+d}, \qquad (11.10)$$

where a, b, c, and d are integers and $ad - bc = \pm 1$. Then

$$E_r\left(\frac{at'+b}{ct'+d}\right) = \Sigma' \frac{1}{\{m[(at'+b)/(ct'+d)]+n\}^{2r}}$$

$$= (ct+d)^{2r} \Sigma' \frac{1}{[m(at'+b)+n(ct'+d)]^{2r}}$$

$$= (ct+d)^{2r} \Sigma' \frac{1}{[(am+cn)t'+(bm+dn)]^{2r}}. \qquad (11.11)$$

As m and n go through all allowable values, the quantities $am + cn$ and $bm + dn$ also go through this set of values, in a different order, of course. This follows from the fact that the equations

$$am + cn = m',$$

$$bm + dn = n', \tag{11.12}$$

has a unique set of integer solutions whenever m' and n' are integers, by virtue of the assumption that $ad - bc = \pm 1$.

We thus obtain the remarkable result that

$$E_r \left(\frac{at + b}{ct + d} \right) = (ct + d)^{2r} E_r(t). \tag{11.13}$$

The question naturally arises as to the connection between these functions and the theta functions. There is indeed a close connection, but one we shall not examine since any such investigation would take us too far afield.

Let us now briefly discuss the Hardy-Littlewood-Ramanujan circle method. Consider the function

$$f(z) = \sum_{n=0}^{\infty} z^{n^2}, \qquad |z| < 1. \tag{11.14}$$

Then

$$f(z)^k = \sum_{n=0}^{\infty} r_k(n) z^n, \tag{11.15}$$

where $r_k(n)$ is the number of representations of the integer n as a sum of k squares. It follows that

$$r_k(n) = \frac{1}{2\pi i} \int_C f(z)^k z^{-(n+1)} \, dz, \tag{11.16}$$

where C is the circumference of a circle lying inside the unit circle, and including the point $z = 0$.

It is to be expected that as C approaches the unit circle, certain singularities of $f(z)$ will contribute more heavily than others to the value of $r_k(n)$ for large n. This is actually the case, and the formulas of section 9 combined with (11.6) yield accurate enough estimates for this method to be efficient.

In place of $f(z)$, we can use the function

$$\phi(t) = \sum_{n=-\infty}^{\infty} e^{n^2 \pi i t}, \tag{11.17}$$

$t = t_1 + is$, and integrate along the line $0 \le t_1 \le 2$, in place of the integration along C.

Comments and References

See

Fueter, R., *Vorlesungen über die singularen Moduln und die komplexe Multiplikation der elliptischen Funktionen*, vol. 1. Leipzig: 1924.

Hecke, E., *Dirichlet Series, Modular Functions and Quadratic Forms*. Edwards Bros., 1938.

The strong impetus to the study of automorphic functions actually came from another direction as a result of studies by Fuchs on the ratio of solutions of particular second order linear differential equations. See

Schlesinger, L., *Handbuch der Theorie der lineare Differentialgleichungen*. Leipzig: 1897.

That the Eisenstein series must be related to the theta functions is clear from the definition of the Weierstrassian elliptic functions. The importance of the series resides in the fact that similar series can be formed in more general situations involving functions of several complex variables where the corresponding elliptic or hyperelliptic functions cannot be defined in the same way. See

Hecke, E., *Mathematische Werke*. Göttingen: 1959,

where a number of papers containing discussions of generalized Eisenstein series may be found.

For the details of the circle method, and other applications, all of which require skillful and delicate analysis, see

Hardy, G. H., *Ramanujan*, chap. 9. Cambridge: Cambridge Univ. Press,

12. The Constant c

Suppose that we had not been lucky enough to evaluate the constant c directly. We would then have the result

$$\sum_{n=-\infty}^{\infty} e^{-n^2 t} = \left(\frac{c}{\sqrt{t}}\right) \sum_{n=-\infty}^{\infty} e^{-\pi^2 n^2/t}, \tag{12.1}$$

where c is an unknown constant. By letting t assume an appropriate value, we should be able to evaluate c. A most convenient value is the limiting value $t = 0$.

Write

$$\left(\sum_{n=-\infty}^{\infty} e^{-n^2 t}\right)^2 = \sum_{m,n} e^{-(m^2+n^2)t}$$

$$= \sum_{n=0}^{\infty} r_n e^{-nt}, \tag{12.2}$$

where r_n is the number-theoretic function defined by the expression

$$r_n = \sum_{k^2+l^2=n} 1$$

where positive and negative integral and zero values of k and l are allowed.

Let us merely sketch the way we would now proceed to determine c. Geometrically, the sum $\sum_{n=0}^{N} r_n$ in 12.3 represents the number of lattice points inside the circle of radius $\sqrt{N}$ and center the origin. Asymptotically, as $n \to \infty$, the number of such points is equal to the area of the circle. Hence,

$$\sum_{n=0}^{\infty} r_n \sim \pi N. \qquad (12.4)$$

Using this result, it follows from standard Abelian arguments in the theory of power series that as $t \to 0$,

$$\sum_{n=0}^{\infty} r_n e^{-nt} \sim \frac{\pi}{t}. \qquad (12.5)$$

On the other hand 12.1 tells us that

$$\left(\sum_{n=-\infty}^{\infty} e^{-n^2 t} \right)^2 \sim \frac{c}{t} \qquad (12.6)$$

as $t \to 0$. Hence $c = \sqrt{\pi}$.

Comments and References

For the background in the theory of power series, see

Titchmarsh, E. C., *Theory of Functions*. Oxford: Oxford Univ. Press, 1939.

For the result concerning lattice-points in a circle, see

Hardy, G. H., and Wright, E. M., *An Introduction to the Theory of Numbers*. p. 268. Oxford: Oxford Univ. Press, 1945.

13. The Heat Equation

Let us now change the mood completely. In place of an analytic approach based upon Fourier series, let us use some results from mathematical physics to present an entirely different approach to the proof of the transformation formula for the theta functions.

It turns out that the theta functions play a basic role in the study of the linear partial differential equations of parabolic type,

$$\frac{\partial u}{\partial t} = \frac{\partial^2 u}{\partial x^2}, \qquad (13.1)$$

the one-dimensional heat equation or diffusion equation.

Suppose that we wish to determine the solution of 13.1 satisfying the initial and boundary conditions

(a) $u(x, 0) = f(x)$,

(b) $u(0, t) = u(\pi, t) = 0, \qquad t > 0.$ \qquad (13.2)

The linearity of the equation enables us to utilize the method of superposition. Consider first the particular solutions of 13.1

$$u_n(x, t) = e^{-n^2 t} \sin nx, \tag{13.3}$$

which satisfy 13.1 and 13.2 (b). Since any linear combination of solutions is a solution, we meet the condition of 13.2 (a) by forming the infinite series

$$u(x, t) = \sum_{n=1}^{\infty} f_n e^{-n^2 t} \sin nx, \tag{13.4}$$

where the f_n are to be chosen so that

$$u(x, 0) = \sum_{n=1}^{\infty} f_n \sin nx = f(x). \tag{13.5}$$

The validation of this analysis is, as to be expected, nontrivial. Since we are interested only in presenting a formal rationale for the transformation formula, we shall not bother in these few sections with rigorous particulars.

Using the orthogonality of the functions $\sin nx$, $n = 1, 2, \ldots$, over the interval $[0, \pi]$, we have

$$f_n = \frac{2}{\pi} \int_0^{\pi} f(x_1) \sin nx_1 \, dx_1. \tag{13.6}$$

Hence, our candidate for the solution of 13.1 together with the boundary conditions of 13.2 is

$$u(x, t) = \sum_{n=1}^{\infty} e^{-n^2 t} \left[\frac{2}{\pi} \int_0^{\pi} f(x_1) \sin nx_1 \, dx_1 \right] \sin nx, \tag{13.7}$$

or

$$u(x, t) = \frac{2}{\pi} \int_0^{\pi} f(x_1) \left[\sum_{n=1}^{\infty} e^{-n^2 t} \sin nx \sin nx_1 \right] dx_1, \tag{13.8}$$

or, finally,

$$u(x, t) = \frac{1}{\pi} \int_0^{\pi} f(x_1) \left[\sum_{n=1}^{\infty} e^{-n^2 t} \cos n(x - x_1) - \sum_{n=1}^{\infty} e^{-n^2 t} \cos n(x + x_1) \right] dx_1. \tag{13.9}$$

We see then the intimate relation between the solutions of the heat equation and the theta functions.

Comments and References

For a classical discussion of the problem of determining when

$$\lim_{t\to 0} u(x,\,t) = f(x),$$

see

Fejer, L., *Math. Ann.*, **58** (1904) 51.

For a further discussion of these matters, see

Doetsch, G., *Theorie und Anwendung der Laplace-Transformation*. New York: Dover Publ. Co., 1943.

14. Formal Derivation of Theorem 1

Since the theta functions can be generated by means of the linear partial differential equation, it is to be expected that the basic properties of these functions can be obtained directly from this source. Although this is the case as far as many properties are concerned, as mentioned above, we shall content ourselves with a purely formal presentation.

Consider the equation

$$\frac{\partial u}{\partial t} = \frac{\partial^2 u}{\partial x^2}, \tag{14.1}$$

and let us seek a solution satisfying the following two conditions :

(a) $u(x,\,t)$ is periodic in x with period one;

(b) $u(x,\,0) = \delta(x)$ (the Dirac delta function) in $-\frac{1}{2} \le x \le \frac{1}{2}$. $\tag{14.2}$

The "function" $\delta(x)$ is defined in $[-\frac{1}{2},\,\frac{1}{2}]$ by the properties

(a) $\delta(x) = 0, \quad x \ne 0,$

(b) $\displaystyle\int_{-1/2}^{1/2} g(x)\,\delta(x)\,dx = g(0) \qquad$ (projection property).

The "solution" to this problem is

$$u(x,\,t) = \sum_{n=1}^{\infty} e^{-n^2\pi^2 t} \sin n\pi x. \tag{14.3}$$

We are, of course, using the term "solution" in a generalized sense, one that can be made clear either by means of the theory of distributions, or the concept of generalized solutions of partial differential equations.

On the other hand, we have another way of constructing a solution to the foregoing problem. The function

$$v(x,\,t) = \frac{e^{-x^2/4t}}{t^{1/2}\pi^{1/2}} \tag{14.4}$$

is, as is easily verified, a solution of the partial differential equation. It represents what physicists call a "similarity solution."

This solution has the properties of $\delta(x)$ at $t = 0$. Namely,

(a) $\lim_{t \to 0} v(x, t) = 0, \qquad x \neq 0,$

(b) $\lim_{t \to 0} v(x, t) = \infty, \qquad x = 0,$ \hfill (14.5)

and, it is not difficult to show that

$$\lim_{t \to 0} \int_{-1/2}^{1/2} v(x, t) f(x) \, dx = f(0), \qquad (14.6)$$

provided that $f(x)$ is continuous at $x = 0$.

In order to meet the condition of periodicity, we use the same device employed in the derivation of the Poisson summation formula. We form the sum

$$w(x, t) = \sum_{n=-\infty}^{\infty} v(x + n, t)$$

$$= \frac{1}{\sqrt{\pi t}} \sum_{n=-\infty}^{\infty} e^{-(n+x)^2/4t}. \qquad (14.7)$$

Since $v(x, t)$ satisfies the partial differential equation of 14.1, the function $v(x + n, t)$ satisfies this equation for each n. Hence, $w(x, t)$ satisfies the equation. Furthermore, it is easy to see that it has the same boundary and initial conditions as $u(x, t)$. It is thus plausible that $u(x, t) = w(x, t)$ for $t > 0$.

Comments and References

The two forms of particular solutions, $e^{-n^2\pi^2 t} \sin n\pi x$, and $e^{-x^2/4t}/t^{1/2}$, are manifestations of a general principle that partial differential equations have similarity solutions for small times and separation-of-variables solutions for large t.

The functional equation for the theta functions, particular solutions of the heat equation, is a special case of a far more general transformation formula valid for general solutions of the heat equation.

Let $u(x, y, z, t)$ be a particular solution of the three-dimensional heat equation

$$\frac{1}{a^2} \frac{\partial u}{\partial t} = \frac{\partial^2 u}{\partial x^2} + \frac{\partial^2 u}{\partial y^2} + \frac{\partial^2 u}{\partial z^2}.$$

Then the function

$$U(x, y, z, t) = t^{-3/2} u\left(\frac{x}{t}, \frac{y}{t}, \frac{z}{t}, \frac{-1}{t}\right) \exp - \left(\frac{x^2 + y^2 + z^2}{4at}\right)$$

is also a solution. There are corresponding results for the n-dimensional heat equation, and analogous results for the wave equation.

Comments and References

See

Whittaker, E. T., and Watson, G. N., *A Course of Modern Analysis*, 4th ed., p. 402, Exer. 16, 18, 19. Cambridge: Cambridge Univ. Press, 1935.

We have presented the foregoing method of establishing transformation formulae, since it has been used by Maass and Siegel to establish some important identities which to date have not been derived by any other means. See

Maass, H., "Über eine neue Art von nichtanalytischen automorphen Funktionen und die Bestimmung Dirichletschen Reihen durch Funktionalgleichungen," *Math. Ann.*, **121** (1949) 141.
Siegel, C. L., "Indefinite quadratische Formen und Funktionentheorie, I." *Math. Ann.*, **124** (1951).

15. The Laplace Transform

In our use of Fourier series, we have emphasized the use of structural features of a function. Let us now use another powerful method, that of *analytic paraphrase*. A relation which is difficult to establish in one set of variables may be quite transparent in another set.

Let us review the basic properties of the most important of all transformations, the Laplace transform.

Let $f(t)$ be an integrable function of t defined for $0 < t < \infty$, and consider the function of s defined by the relation

$$F(s) = \int_0^\infty e^{-st} f(t) \, dt. \tag{15.1}$$

Provided that $f(t)$ satisfies a relation of the form $|f(t)| = 0(e^{bt})$ as $t \to \infty$, $F(s)$ will be an analytic function of s for $Re(s) > b$.

The great merit of this relation between $f(t)$ and $F(s)$ lies in the fact that in many significant cases it reduces the level of transcendence of $f(t)$. Solutions of differential equations are reduced to solutions of linear algebraic equations and solutions of partial differential equations are reduced to solutions of ordinary differential equations.

Consequently, it is always worthwhile to attempt to derive an identity in in t space by examining the equivalent identity in s space. As we shall see, familiar identities in s space, readily established, are equivalent to recondite identities in t space.

As in the application of the theory of Fourier series, a basic role is played by a uniqueness theorem. We shall merely state the result, referring to references given below for proofs.

Theorem 4 (Lerch's theorem): *If f(t) is continuous for t > 0, and*

(a) $\int_0^\infty e^{-at} \, |f(t)| \, dt < \infty,$ *for some a,*

(b) $F(s) = \int_0^\infty e^{-st} f(t) \, dt = 0,$ (15.2)

for s > a, then f(t) = 0 for t > 0.

From this it follows that if

$$\int_0^\infty e^{-st} f_1(t) \, dt = \int_0^\infty e^{-st} f_2(t) \, dt \qquad (15.3)$$

for $Re(s) > a$, then $f_1(t) = f_2(t)$ for all $t > 0$, provided that $f_1(t)$ and $f_2(t)$ are continuous for $t > 0$.

Comments and References

We shall use below the more precise result that $f_1(t) = f_2(t)$ at every common point of continuity, provided only that we assume that $f_1(t)$ and $f_2(t)$ are Lebesgue integrable.

The classical references for the theory of the Laplace transform and the closely related theory of the Fourier integral are

Bochner, S., *Vorlesungen über Fouriersche Integrale.* Leipzig: 1932.
Doetsch, G., *Theorie und Anwendung der Laplace-Transformation.* New York: Dover Publ. Co., 1943.
Widder, D. V., *The Laplace Transform.* Princeton: Princeton Univ. Press.
Titchmarsh, E. C., *Introduction to the Theory of Fourier Integrals.* Oxford: Oxford Univ. Press, 1937.

The method discussed above for establishing identities was a favorite of Ramanujan's.

16.   Another Infinite Integral

Prior to our subsequent use of the Laplace transform to establish the theta function transformation formula, a method due to Hamburger, we wish to devote some attention to the interesting infinite integral

$$I(u, v) = \int_0^\infty e^{[-(u/t)-vt]} \frac{dt}{\sqrt{t}}, \qquad (16.1)$$

where $Re(u) > 0$, $Re(v) > 0$. As before, it is sufficient to consider the case where u, v are both real and positive. We are then examining the Laplace transform of the function

$$f(t) = \frac{e^{-x^2/4t}}{t^{1/2}}, \qquad (16.2)$$

the function

$$F(s) = \int_0^\infty e^{-st - (x^2/4t)} \frac{dt}{\sqrt{t}} \tag{16.3}$$

for positive s.

Our first two evaluations will be based upon ingenuity. A third proof will use a more pedestrian but systematic technique.

We start with the result discussed in Section 8,

$$\sqrt{\pi} = \int_{-\infty}^\infty e^{-u^2} \, du, \tag{16.4}$$

and set

$$u = v - \frac{y}{v}, \qquad y > 0. \tag{16.5}$$

Since $du/dv = 1 + (y/v^2) > 0$, this is a one-to-one transformation taking the interval $-\infty < u < \infty$ into $-0 < v < \infty$. The relation in 16.4 becomes

$$\sqrt{\pi} = \int_0^\infty e^{-[v + (y/v)]^2} \left(1 + \frac{y}{v^2}\right) dv$$

$$= e^{2y} \int_0^\infty e^{-[v^2 + (y^2/v^2)]} \left(1 + \frac{y}{v^2}\right) dv. \tag{16.6}$$

Hence

$$\sqrt{\pi} \, e^{-2y} = \int_0^\infty e^{-[v^2 + (y^2/v^2)]} \, dv + y \int_0^\infty e^{-[v^2 + (y^2/v^2)]} \frac{dv}{v^2}. \tag{16.7}$$

In the second integral make the change of variable $v = y/v_1$, obtaining the equation

$$y \int_0^\infty e^{-[v^2 + (y^2/v^2)]} \frac{dv}{v^2} = \int_0^\infty e^{-[(y^2/v_1^2) + v_1^2]} \frac{dv_1}{v_1^2}. \tag{16.8}$$

Combining these results, 16.7 yields

$$\frac{\sqrt{\pi} \, e^{-2y}}{2} = \int_0^\infty e^{-[v^2 + (y^2/v^2)]} \, dv. \tag{16.9}$$

From this, simple changes of variable yield the desired result

$$\frac{\sqrt{\pi} \, e^{-x\sqrt{s}}}{\sqrt{s}} = \int_0^\infty e^{-[st + (x^2/4t)]} \frac{dt}{\sqrt{t}}. \tag{16.10}$$

Alternatively, we can start with

$$\frac{I}{2} = \int_0^\infty e^{-a^2/t^2 - b^2 t^2} \, dt, \tag{16.11}$$

and put $w = (a/t) - bt$, a, $b > 0$. Then

$$t = \frac{w + (w^2 + 4ab)^{1/2}}{2b},$$

$$dt = \frac{1}{2b}\left[1 + \frac{w}{(w^2 + 4ab)^{1/2}}\right]. \tag{16.12}$$

This is a one-to-one transformation with w going from $+\infty$ to $-\infty$ as t goes from 0 to ∞. Hence

$$\frac{I}{2} = \int_{-\infty}^{\infty} \frac{e^{-w^2-2ab}}{2b}\left[1 + \frac{w}{(w^2 + 4ab)^{1/2}}\right] dw$$

$$= \frac{1}{2b}\int_{-\infty}^{\infty} e^{-w^2-2ab}\, dw. \tag{16.13}$$

From this the desired result is immediate.

Comments and References

The first proof is contained in the book by Doetsch, referred to above. The second proof whose origin is obscure I owe to the kindness of L. Mordell. The relation in 16.10 was extensively used by Hecke to derive a number of important results. The more general integral

$$J_a(x) = \int_C e^{-xz-(1/z)}\frac{dz}{z^a}$$

(where C is a particular contour) is a Bessel function. The particular kind of Bessel function is determined by the contour which is used. These integrals were also used by Voronoi in his researches on the asymptotic behavior of $\Sigma_{n<N}\, d(n)$ as $N \to \infty$ (the Dirichlet divisor problem). For a number of identities involving these functions, based upon the transformation formulas of the theta functions, see

Bellman, R., "Generalized Eisenstein series and non-analytic automorphic functions." *Proc. nat. Acad. Sci.*, Washington, D. C., **36** (1950) 356.

17.   The Transformed Transformation Formula

Let us begin with the special identity

$$\sum_{n=-\infty}^{\infty} e^{-tn^2} = \sqrt{\frac{\pi}{t}}\sum_{n=-\infty}^{\infty} e^{-\pi^2 n^2/t}. \tag{17.1}$$

The Laplace transform of the function on the left is readily obtained. We have, as a consequence of uniform convergence of series and absolute convergence of the integral, here and below,

$$\int_0^\infty e^{-st} \left[\sum_{n=-\infty}^\infty e^{-tn^2} \right] dt = \frac{1}{s} + 2 \sum_{n=1}^\infty \frac{1}{(n^2 + s)}, \tag{17.2}$$

for $Re(s) > 0$. Using the infinite integral we have just evaluated, the Laplace transform of the function on the right side of 17.1 is given by

$$\sqrt{\pi} \int_0^\infty e^{-st} \left[\frac{1}{\sqrt{t}} + 2 \sum_{n=1}^\infty \frac{e^{-n^2\pi^2/t}}{\sqrt{t}} \right] dt = \frac{\pi}{\sqrt{s}} + \frac{2\pi}{\sqrt{s}} \sum_{n=1}^\infty e^{-\pi n \sqrt{s}}, \tag{17.3}$$

for $Re(s) > 0$.

Consequently, the s space version of 17.1 is the identity

$$\frac{1}{s} + 2 \sum_{n=1}^\infty \frac{1}{(n^2 + s)} = \frac{\pi}{\sqrt{s}} + \frac{2\pi}{\sqrt{s}} \sum_{n=1}^\infty e^{-\pi n \sqrt{s}}. \tag{17.4}$$

The right-hand side is readily summed :

$$\frac{\pi}{\sqrt{s}} + \frac{2\pi}{\sqrt{s}} \sum_{n=1}^\infty e^{-\pi n \sqrt{s}} = \frac{\pi}{\sqrt{s}} + \frac{2\pi}{\sqrt{s}} \frac{e^{-\pi\sqrt{s}}}{(1 - e^{-\pi\sqrt{s}})} = \frac{\pi}{\sqrt{s}} \frac{(1 + e^{-\pi\sqrt{s}})}{(1 - e^{-\pi\sqrt{s}})}. \tag{17.5}$$

The left-hand side of 17.4 represents a partial fraction development. We see then that the transformation formula for the theta function, a rather mysterious formula in the t plane, is merely a reflection on another screen of the decomposition into partial fractions of one of the elementary functions of analysis. For the sake of completeness, we shall derive this decomposition in the next section.

Comments and References

This proof of the transformation formula is due to Hamburger. See

Hamburger, H., "Über einige Beziehungen die mit der Funktionalgleichung der Riemannsche ζ-Funktion aequivalent sind." *Math. Ann.*, **85** (1922) 129.

The formula

$$\sum_{n=-\infty}^\infty e^{-\pi t n^2} = t^{-1/2} \sum_{n=-\infty}^\infty e^{-\pi n^2/t}$$

leads, upon raising to the kth power, to the relation

$$\sum_{n=-\infty}^\infty \exp\left[-\pi t \sum_{m=1}^k n_m^2 \right] = t^{-k/2} \sum_{n=-\infty}^\infty \exp\left[-\frac{\pi}{t} \sum_{m=1}^k n_m^2 \right].$$

This relation was extended by Hecke and Schoeneberg to the identity

$$\sum_n P(n_1, n_2, ..., n_k) \exp\left(-\pi t \sum_{m=1}^{k} n_m^2\right)$$

$$= i^g t^{-k/2-g} \sum_n P(n_1, n_2, ..., n_k) \exp\left(-\frac{\pi}{t} \sum_{m=1}^{k} n_m^2\right),$$

where $P(x_1, x_2, ..., x_k)$ is any homogeneous polynomial of degree g satisfying the Laplacian $\Delta P = 0$.
  See

Hecke, E., *Math.-Fys. Medd.*, **17** (1940.
Schoeneberg, B., *Math. Ann.*, **116** (1939) 511.

  These results were extended, using transform techniques, by Bochner.

Bochner, S., "Theta functions with spherical harmonics." *Proc. nat. Acad. Sci.*, Washington, D. C. **37** (1951) 804.

18. Infinite Products and By-products

  There are, as might be expected, several elegant ways of establishing the relation in 17.5. An interesting method, which is a forerunner of a procedure we shall employ subsequently, is based upon the fundamental identity

$$\sin x = x \prod_{n=1}^{\infty} \left(1 - \frac{x^2}{n^2\pi^2}\right), \tag{18.1}$$

which we take to be known. Taking logarithms of both sides, we have

$$\log \sin x = \log x + \sum_{n=1}^{\infty} \log\left(1 - \frac{x^2}{n^2\pi^2}\right). \tag{18.2}$$

Differentiating with respect to x, we obtain the relation

$$\cot x = \frac{1}{x} - \sum_{n=1}^{\infty} \frac{2x}{n^2\pi^2 - x^2}. \tag{18.3}$$

Setting $x = iy$, we have

$$\frac{e^y + e^{-y}}{e^y - e^{-y}} = \frac{1}{y} + \sum_{n=1}^{\infty} \frac{2y}{y^2 + n^2\pi^2}, \tag{18.4}$$

readily seen to be equivalent to the desired result.

19.　The General Theta Function Transformation

We leave it to the reader to derive the more general identity

$$
\frac{\cos(2x-1)\sqrt{s}}{\sqrt{-s}\,\sin\sqrt{-s}} = \frac{1}{\sqrt{s}}\left\{ e^{-2x\sqrt{s}} + \sum_{n=1}^{\infty} e^{-2(n+x)\sqrt{s}} + \sum_{n=1}^{\infty} e^{-2(n-x)\sqrt{s}}\right\}
$$

$$
= \frac{1}{s} + 2\sum_{n=1}^{\infty} \frac{\cos 2n\,\pi x}{s + n^2\pi^2}, \tag{19.1}
$$

using either partial fractions or the theory of Fourier series, and then to verify that this result is the Laplace transform of the identity

$$
1 + 2\sum_{m=1}^{\infty} e^{-m^2\pi^2 t}\cos 2m\pi x = \frac{1}{\sqrt{\pi t}}\sum_{n=-\infty}^{\infty} e^{-(n+x)^2/t}. \tag{19.2}
$$

Comments and References

For the details and further discussion, see p. 176 of the book by Doetsch.

20.　Some Results of Doetsch

The basic and fruitful idea of obtaining paraphrases of identities by means of suitable transforms can be made to yield a number of elegant results, all equivalent to the fundamental transformation formula for the theta function.

Let $J_0(x)$ represent, as usual, the Bessel function of order zero,

$$
J_0(x) = \sum_{k=0}^{\infty} \frac{(-1)^k}{(k!)^2}\left(\frac{x}{2}\right)^{2k}. \tag{20.1}
$$

Then it is easy to see by means of a term-by-term integration that

$$
\int_0^{\infty} e^{-st} J_0[(n+v)\sqrt{t}]\,dt = \frac{e^{-(n+v)^2/4s}}{s}. \tag{20.2}
$$

Let us also introduce the sequence of functions

$$
\begin{aligned}
g_m(t) &= 0, &0 \le t \le 4m^2\pi^2,\\
&= \frac{1}{(t - 4m^2\pi^2)^{1/2}}, &t > 4m^2\pi^2,
\end{aligned} \tag{20.3}
$$

for $m = 0, 1, \dots$.

Then, for $s > 0$,

$$
\int_0^{\infty} e^{-st} g_m(t)\,dt = \int_0^{\infty} e^{-s(t+4m^2\pi)^2}\,\frac{dt}{\sqrt{t}}
$$

$$
= \sqrt{\frac{\pi}{s}}\, e^{-4m^2\pi^2 s}. \tag{20.4}
$$

Using the functional equation for θ_3, we see that

$$\int_0^\infty e^{-st} \left\{ \sum_{n=-\infty}^\infty J_0[(n+v)\sqrt{t}\,] \right\} dt = 2 \int_0^\infty e^{-st} \left[g_0(t) + \sum_{m=1}^\infty g_m(t) \cos 2m\pi v \right] dt$$

$$(20.5)$$

for $s > 0$. Hence, if $x > 0$, $x \neq 2m\pi$, $0 < v < 1$, we have

$$\frac{1}{2} \sum_{n=-\infty}^\infty J_0[(n+v)x] = \frac{1}{x} + 2 \sum_{m=1}^p \frac{\cos 2m\pi v}{\sqrt{x^2 - 4m^2\pi^2}} \qquad (20.6)$$

where $p = (x/2\pi)$.

Doetsch gives a number of extensions of this result involving the Bessel function $J_v(x)$ and some interesting particularizations. Let us cite merely one of these:

$$\frac{1}{\pi} \sum_{n=-\infty}^\infty \frac{\sin(n+v)x}{n+v} = \frac{\sin(2p+1)\pi v}{\sin \pi v}, \qquad (20.7)$$

$0 < v < 1$, $x \neq 2m\pi$, $p = [x/2\pi]$.

Comments and References

Doetsch, G., "Summatorische Eigenschaften der Besselschen Funktionen und andere Funktionalrelationen, die mit der linearen Transformationsformel der Thetafunktion äquivalent sind." *Compos. math.*, **1** (1935) 85.

21. Results of Kober-Erdelyi

The foregoing result by Doetsch was generalized by Kober, as follows:

$$\sum_{n=-\infty}^\infty \frac{J_v(2\pi \mid n+x \mid \sqrt{t}\,)}{\mid n+x \mid^v} e^{2\pi i \beta(n+x)} \qquad (21.1)$$

$$= \frac{t^{-v/2}\pi^{v-(1/2)}}{\Gamma[v + (\frac{1}{2})]} \sum_{\mid n+\beta \mid < \sqrt{t}} e^{-2\pi i n x} [t - (n+\beta)^2]^{v-(1/2)}. \qquad (21.1)$$

This result was taken up by Erdelyi who showed that a variety of transforms involving Hankel functions and Whittaker functions could be used to obtain a number of corresponding results. The paper by Erdelyi also contains some work on dual integral equations and summation formulae.

Comments and References

Kober, H., "Transformationsformeln gewissen Besselscher Reihen, Beziehungen zu Zeta-Funktionen." *Math. Z.*, **39** (1935) 609.

Erdelyi, A., "Gewisse Reihentransformationen die mit der linearen Transformationsformel der Thetafunktion zusammenhangen." *Compos. math.*, **4** (1937) 406.

22. The Mellin Transform

We shall tie a number of apparently unrelated threads together by means of a transform which is really a special case of the Laplace transform, the Mellin transform. This functional transformation is defined by means of the formula

$$M(s) = \int_0^\infty f(x)\, x^{s-1}\, dx. \tag{22.1}$$

With suitable restrictions upon the function $f(x)$ at $x = 0$ and $x = \infty$, this relation yields a function $M(s)$ which is analytic in a region given by $a < Re(s) < b$. The most important example is the gamma function

$$\Gamma(s) = \int_0^\infty e^{-x} x^{s-1}\, dx, \tag{22.2}$$

analytic for $Re(s) > 0$.

One of the most frequently used properties of the Mellin transform is the simple relation

$$\int_0^\infty f(xy)\, x^{s-1}\, dx = y^{-s} \int_0^\infty f(x)\, x^{s-1}\, dx, \tag{22.3}$$

valid for $y > 0$. This result will be used below in connection with a class of Dirichlet series.

The Laplace transform

$$F(s) = \int_0^\infty e^{-sx} f(x)\, dx \tag{22.4}$$

possesses the inversion formula

$$f(x) = \frac{1}{2\pi i} \int_C F(s)\, e^{sx}\, ds, \tag{22.5}$$

where C is a contour to the right of all of the singularities of $F(s)$, usually taken to be a line $s = b + it$, $-\infty < t < \infty$. Various conditions for the validity of this formula may be found in the texts cited above.

The change of variable $e^{-x} = y$ converts 22.4 into the relation

$$F(s) = \int_0^1 y^{s-1} f\left(\log \frac{1}{y}\right) dy$$

$$= \int_0^\infty y^{s-1} g(y)\, dy, \tag{22.6}$$

Mellin transform.

From this result, or directly, we see that an inversion formula for the Mellin transform is

$$f(x) = \frac{1}{2\pi i} \int_C M(s)\, x^{-s}\, ds, \tag{22.7}$$

where C is usually a line $s = b + it$, lying within the strip of analyticity of $M(s)$. A result we shall use below is the following:

Theorem 5: *Let* $\phi(s) = \phi(\sigma + it)$ *be regular in* $\lambda < \sigma < \mu$, *and*

$$\int_{-\infty}^{\infty} |\phi(\sigma + it)| \, dt \tag{22.8}$$

be bounded in this strip. Then, for $\lambda < \sigma < \mu$,

$$f(x) = \frac{1}{2\pi i} \int_C \phi(s) \, x^{-s} \, ds, \tag{22.9}$$

defines for positive x a function $f(x)$ such that in this strip

$$\phi(s) = \int_0^{\infty} f(x) \, x^{s-1} \, dx. \tag{22.10}$$

This integral converges absolutely.

Here C is the straight line $s = \sigma + it$ and the integration is over $-\infty < t < \infty$.

Comments and References

The result above is Satz 47 on p. 156 of the book by Bochner. For some recent applications of transforms to theta functions, see

Barrucand, P., "Fonctions elliptiques et transformations de Fourier et de Mellin." *C. R. Acad. Sci., Paris,* **250** (1960) 269.

Other results concerning the Mellin transform may be found in the book by Doetsch and in

Titchmarsh, E. C., *Theory of Fourier Integrals.* Oxford: Oxford Univ. Press, 1937.

23. An Application of the Mellin Transform

As an example of the many ways in which the Mellin transform, like the Laplace transform, can be used to derive identities, let us return to the evaluation of the integral

$$f(x) = \int_0^{\infty} e^{-t-(x^2/4t)} \, \frac{dt}{\sqrt{t}}, \tag{23.1}$$

(an integral we have already met in Section 16).

Taking the Mellin transform of both sides, we have

$$\int_0^{\infty} f(x) \, x^{s-1} \, dx = \int_0^{\infty} x^{s-1} \left[\int_0^{\infty} e^{-t-(x^2/4t)} \, \frac{dt}{\sqrt{t}} \right] dx$$

$$= \int_0^{\infty} \frac{e^{-t}}{\sqrt{t}} \left[\int_0^{\infty} x^{s-1} \, e^{-x^2/4t} \, dx \right] dt. \tag{23.2}$$

Since

$$\int_0^\infty x^{s-1} e^{-x^2/4t}\, dx = 2^{s-1}\, t^{s/2} \int_0^\infty e^{-w}\, w^{s/(2-1)}\, dw$$

$$= 2^{s-1}\, t^{s/2}\, \Gamma\left(\frac{s}{2}\right), \tag{23.3}$$

using a simple change of variable, we end up with the result

$$\int_0^\infty f(x)\, x^{s-1}\, dx = 2^{s-1}\, \Gamma\left(\frac{s}{2}\right) \int_0^\infty e^{-t}\, t^{(s/2-1/2)}\, dt$$

$$= 2^{s-1}\, \Gamma\left(\frac{s}{2}\right) \Gamma\left(\frac{s}{2}+\frac{1}{2}\right). \tag{23.4}$$

The duplication formula for the gamma function

$$\sqrt{\pi}\, \Gamma(s) = 2^{s-1}\, \Gamma\left(\frac{s}{2}\right) \Gamma\left(\frac{s}{2}+\frac{1}{2}\right) \tag{23.5}$$

shows the equality of the Mellin transforms of $f(x)$ and the function $\sqrt{\pi} e^{-x}$, invoking standard uniqueness theorems. Hence

$$\sqrt{\pi}\, e^{-x} = \int_0^\infty e^{-t-(x^2/4t)}\, \frac{dt}{\sqrt{t}}. \tag{23.6}$$

Alternatively, we can use this formula to derive the duplication formula.

Comments and References

For the duplication formula, see Whittaker and Watson, p. 240. The above result is due to Legendre. The general result

$$(2\pi)^{(n-1)/2}\, n^{(1/2)-nz}\, \Gamma(nz) = \Gamma(z)\, \Gamma\left(z+\frac{1}{n}\right) \Gamma\left(z+\frac{2}{n}\right) \cdots \Gamma\left(z+\frac{n-1}{n}\right)$$

is due to Gauss. Using this formula, we can obtain a representation of the form

$$\exp\left(-x^{1/n}\right) = k_n \int_0^\infty \cdots \int_0^\infty \exp\left(-\frac{(t_1+t_2+\cdots+t_{n-1})-x}{t_1 t_2 \cdots t_{n-1}}\right)$$

$$\times\, t_1^{a_1} t_2^{a_2} \cdots t_{n-1}^{a_{n-1}}\, dt_1 \cdots dt_{n-1}$$

for suitable choice of the exponents $a_1, a_2, \ldots, a_{n-1}$, where k_n is a constant independent of x. We leave this to the reader.

24. The Riemann Zeta Function

Let us now pursue an apparently tangential path. We wish to consider one of the most fascinating and glamorous functions of analysis, the Riemann zeta function. The connection between this function and theta functions was extensively discussed by Riemann.

This function, $\zeta(s)$, is defined for $Re(s) > 1$ by the simplest of Dirichlet series, the series

$$\zeta(s) = \sum_{n=1}^{\infty} \frac{1}{n^s}. \tag{24.1}$$

Clearly, this defines an analytic function for $Re(s) > 1$. Since the most interesting properties of $\zeta(s)$ are tied to the region $0 \leq Re(s) \leq 1$, let us examine the question of analytic continuation. We shall follow a trail blazed by Riemann, leading from the theta function to the zeta function.

Consider the function

$$g(t) = \sum_{n=1}^{\infty} e^{-n^2 \pi t}, \tag{24.2}$$

whose Mellin transform is readily obtained. For $Re(s) > \frac{1}{2}$, we have

$$\int_0^{\infty} g(t) \, t^{s-1} \, dt = \int_0^{\infty} \left(\sum_{n=1}^{\infty} e^{-n^2 \pi t} \right) t^{s-1} \, dt$$

$$= \sum_{n=1}^{\infty} \frac{1}{n^{2s} \pi^s} \int_0^{\infty} e^{-t} \, t^{s-1} \, dt$$

$$= \frac{\Gamma(s)}{\pi^s} \sum_{n=1}^{\infty} \frac{1}{n^{2s}}. \tag{24.3}$$

(The condition $Re(s) > \frac{1}{2}$ arises in two ways, one is to ensure the convergence of the integral and the other is to ensure the connergence of the series.)

We thus obtain an important representation

$$\frac{\Gamma(s/2)\zeta(s)}{\pi^{s/2}} = \int_0^{\infty} t^{(s/2)-1} \left(\sum_{n=1}^{\infty} e^{-n^2 \pi t} \right) dt, \tag{24.4}$$

valid for $Re(s) > \frac{1}{2}$. To obtain the analytic continuation of $\zeta(s)$ we shall use the functional equation of the theta function.

Write

$$\Gamma\left(\frac{s}{2}\right) \zeta(s) \pi^{-s/2} = \int_0^{\infty} t^{(s/2)-1} g(t) \, dt = \int_0^1 + \int_1^{\infty}. \tag{24.5}$$

In the interval $[0,1]$, let us replace $g(t)$ by its equivalent obtained from the transformation formula,

$$g(t) = -\frac{1}{2} + \frac{1}{2} t^{-1/2} + t^{-1/2} g\left(\frac{1}{t}\right), \tag{24.6}$$

(a result obtained first in Section 9).

Then

$$\frac{\Gamma(s/2)\ \zeta(s)}{\pi^{s/2}} = \int_0^1 \left(-\frac{1}{2} + \frac{t^{-1/2}}{2}\right) t^{(s/2)-1}\ dt + \int_0^1 g\left(\frac{1}{t}\right) t^{(s/2)-(3/2)}\ dt$$

$$+ \int_1^\infty t^{(s/2)-1}\ g(t)\ dt. \qquad (24.7)$$

In the second integral, make the change of variable $t' = 1/t$. Evaluating the first integral, we obtain finally

$$\frac{\Gamma(s/2)\ \zeta(s)}{\pi^{s/2}} = \left(\frac{1}{s-1} - \frac{1}{s}\right) + \int_1^\infty [t^{s/2} + t^{(1-s)/2}]\ g(t)\ \frac{dt}{t}. \qquad (24.8)$$

Since $|g(t)| = 0\ (e^{-\pi t})$ as $t \to \infty$, we see that the integral is an entire function of s.

It follows that $\Gamma(s/2)\ \zeta(s)$ is analytic except at the points $s = 0$ and $s = 1$, where it possesses simple poles. Since $\Gamma(s/2)$ has a simple pole at $s = 0$, we see that $\zeta(s)$ is analytic over the entire s plane, except at $s = 1$, where it possesses a simple pole. Since $\Gamma(\frac{1}{2}) = \sqrt{\pi}$, we see that

$$\zeta(s) = \frac{1}{s-1} + \dots \qquad (24.9)$$

in the neighborhood of $s = 1$, a result we shall use below.

We have thus solved the problem of the analytic continuation of $\zeta(s)$ over the entire s plane. We can, however, obtain much more from the identity of 24.8. Observe that the expression on the right-hand side of 24.8 is invariant under the change of variable $s' = 1 - s$.

It follows that we have the remarkable functional equation

$$\Gamma\left(\frac{s}{2}\right)\pi^{-s/2}\ \zeta(s) = \Gamma\left(\frac{1-s}{2}\right)\pi^{-(1-s)/2}\ \zeta(1-s) \qquad (24.10)$$

for $s \neq 0$ or 1.

Comments and References

This was the second method used by Riemann to derive the functional equation. See

Riemann, B., "Über die Anzahl der Primzahlen unter einer gegebenen Grosse." *Werke*, 2, pp. 145-153, 1892. (Collected Works of Bernhard Riemann, Dover, 1953).

25. An Alternate Form of the Functional Equation

The duplication formula for the gamma function, a result we have already encountered, permits us to write the functional equation in the form

$$\zeta(s) = \frac{2^{s-1}\pi^s\,\zeta(1-s)}{\Gamma(s)\cos(\pi s/2)}.\tag{25.1}$$

To obtain this from 24.10, we must also use the formula

$$\Gamma\left(\frac{1-s}{2}\right)\Gamma\left(\frac{1+s}{2}\right) = \frac{\pi}{\sin\left(\dfrac{\pi(1-s)}{2}\right)}.$$

This is occasionally a more convenient expression to employ.

26. The Riemann Hypothesis

The functional equation of 24.10 shows that the function $\Gamma(s/2)\pi^{-s/2}\,\zeta(s)$ is symmetric about $s = \frac{1}{2}$. Consequently, it is to be expected that this line will play an important role in the theory of the zeta function. On the basis of the functional equation and an asymptotic formula derived in a way we shall subsequently discuss, Riemann conjectured that all of the zeroes of $\Gamma(s/2)\,\zeta(s)$ were on the line $s = \frac{1}{2} + it$.

Despite the apparent simplicity of the function, this statement has never been confirmed or refuted. As a result of the concentrated effort of a number of mathematicians—Hadamard, De La Vallee Poussin, Gronwall, Landau, Hardy, Littlewood, Ingham, Titchmarsh, and Selberg—a great deal has been learned about the distribution of the zeroes of $\zeta(s)$. The calculations of digital computers based upon various formulas confirm the hypothesis as far as they go. Nevertheless, the Riemann hypothesis remains one of the outstanding challenges of mathematics, a prize which has tantalized and eluded some of the most brilliant mathematicians of this century.

The Euler factorization

$$\zeta(s) = \prod_p \left(1 - \frac{1}{p^s}\right)^{-1}, \qquad Re(s) > 1,\tag{26.1}$$

where the product is taken over the primes $p = 2, 3, 5, \ldots$, shows the intimate connection between the analytic properties of $\zeta(s)$ and the distribution of primes. It is an analytic expression of the result of Euclid concerning unique factorization. Although it can be deduced from this expression that $\zeta(s) \neq 0$ for $Re(s) > 1$, further results, meager as they are, are obtained only at great effort.

Comments and References

For a detailed account of the current state of knowledge, see

Titchmarsh, E. C., *The Zeta-Function of Riemann*. Cambridge: Cambridge Univ. Press, 1930.

Hilbert is reputed to have said that the first comment he would make after waking at the end of a thousand year sleep would be, "Is the Riemann hypothesis established yet?"

27.   The Poisson Summation Formula and the Zeta Function

In the foregoing pages we have shown that the Poisson summation formula leads to the transformation formula for the theta function, and thence, following Riemann, to the functional equation for the zeta function.

The reader may suspect, justly, that the Poisson summation formula is capable of establishing the functional equation for the zeta function directly. This is the case, but not trivially. We leave it as a challenge to the reader's ingenuity to carry out this program. One approach can be based upon the use of the function (the Hurwitz zeta function),

$$\zeta(a, x, s) = \sum_{n=-\infty}^{\infty} \frac{e^{2n\pi i x}}{(a+n)^s}, \qquad (27.1)$$

$0 < x < 1, 0 < a < 1, 0 < Re(s) < 1$, considered as a periodic function of a.

Let us complete the chain by showing that the Poisson summation formula can be derived from the functional equation for the zeta function. What is remarkable about this result is that it shows what is so often true in analysis, namely that it is not easy to distinguish between the general and the particular. The apparently more general result, the Poisson summation formula, can actually be derived from the apparently more special result, the functional equation for $\zeta(s)$. Furthermore, this new derivation is far more important than the old, since it indicates how a number of other summation formulae, unrelated to periodicity and Fourier series, can be derived from certain classes of Dirichlet series.

The path we shall follow in a rough fashion was first indicated by Ferrar. Consider the function $g(x)$ defined as follows:

$$g(x) = \sum_{n=1}^{\infty} f(nx), \qquad (27.2)$$

for $x > 0$. Taking Mellin transforms of both sides, we have

$$\int_0^{\infty} g(x) \, x^{s-1} \, dx = \sum_{n=1}^{\infty} \int_0^{\infty} f(nx) \, x^{s-1} \, dx$$

$$= \sum_{n=1}^{\infty} \frac{1}{n^s} \int_0^{\infty} f(x) \, x^{s-1} \, dx$$

$$= \zeta(s) \int_0^{\infty} f(x) \, x^{s-1} \, dx, \qquad (27.3)$$

for $Re(s) > 1$. Let us assume that the Mellin transforms of $f(x)$ and $g(x)$ exist and are analytic for $Re(s) > 1$.

Then, using the inversion formula

$$g(x) = \frac{1}{2\pi i} \int_C \zeta(s) \left[\int_0^{\infty} f(x_1) \, x_1^{s-1} \, dx_1 \right] x^{-s} \, ds, \qquad (27.4)$$

where C is a contour $s = 1 + c + it, \, c > 0$.

Write

$$\phi(s) = \int_0^{\infty} f(x) \, x^{s-1} \, dx,$$

and choose $x = 1$ in 27.4. Then, referring to 27.2, we have

$$\sum_{n=1}^{\infty} f(n) = \frac{1}{2\pi i} \int_C \phi(s) \, \zeta(s) \, ds. \qquad (27.5)$$

Use the functional equation for $\zeta(s)$,

$$\pi^{-s/2} \, \Gamma\left(\frac{s}{2}\right) \zeta(s) = \pi^{(s-1)/2} \, \Gamma\left(\frac{1}{2} - \frac{s}{2}\right) \zeta(1-s). \qquad (27.6)$$

Then 27.5 yields

$$\sum_{n=1}^{\infty} f(n) = \frac{1}{2\pi i} \int_C \phi(s) \, \pi^{s-(1/2)} \frac{\Gamma[(1/2) - (s/2)]}{\Gamma(s/2)} \zeta(1-s) \, ds$$

$$= R_0 + R_1 + \frac{1}{2\pi i} \int_{C_1}, \qquad (27.7)$$

where R_0 and R_1 are the residues at $s = 0$ and $s = 1$, and C_1 denotes the line $s = -b + it, \, b > 0$.

To evaluate the integral along C_1, we write

$$\zeta(1 - s) = \sum_{n=1}^{\infty} n^{s-1}.$$

Thus,

$$\sum_{n=1}^{\infty} f(n) = R_0 + R_1 + \sum_{n=1}^{\infty} \frac{1}{2\pi i} \int_{C_1} \pi^{(s-1/2)} \frac{\Gamma[(1/2) - (s/2)]}{\Gamma(s/2)} \phi(s) \, n^{s-1} \, ds. \qquad (27.8)$$

Move the line of integration in each term back to $s = \beta + it$, $\frac{1}{2} < \beta < 1$, a contour C_2. Then

$$\frac{1}{2\pi i} \int_{C_1} \pi^{s-(1/2)} \frac{\Gamma[(1/2) - (s/2)]}{\Gamma(s/2)} \phi(s)\, n^{s-1}\, ds$$

$$= \frac{1}{2\pi i} \int_{C_2} \pi^{s-(1/2)} \frac{\Gamma[(1/2) - (s/2)]}{\Gamma(s/2)} n^{s-1} \left[\int_0^\infty f(x)\, x^{s-1}\, dx \right] ds$$

$$= \int_0^\infty f(x) \left[\int_{C_2} \frac{\pi^{s-(1/2)}\, \Gamma[(1/2) - (s/2)]\, (nx)^{s-1}}{2\pi i\, \Gamma(s)}\, ds \right] dx$$

$$= 2 \int_0^\infty f(x) \cos 2\pi n x\, dx. \tag{27.9}$$

The integral along C_2 may be evaluated either by the method of residues, or by means of an evaluation of the integral

$$\int_0^\infty x^\alpha \cos xy\, dx \tag{27.10}$$

for $-1 < \alpha < 0$.

Evaluating the residues under the assumption that $\phi(s)$ contributes no singularities, we have

$$R_1 = \phi(1) = \int_0^\infty f(x)\, dx,$$

$$R_0 = -\frac{1}{2} f(+0). \tag{27.11}$$

Hence, the final result is

$$\frac{1}{2} f(+0) + \sum_{n=1}^\infty f(n) = \int_0^\infty f(x)\, dx + 2 \sum_{n=1}^\infty \left[\int_0^\infty f(x) \cos 2n\pi x\, dx \right]. \tag{27.12}$$

Comments and References

A rigorous discussion is contained in

Ferrar, W. L., "Summation formulae and their relation to Dirichlet's series—II." *Compos. math.*, **4** (1936-37) 394.

Ferrar's paper also contains a treatment of what modifications are necessary when $f(x)$ possesses various singularities.

For some interesting applications of the Poisson summation formula, see

Mordell, L. J., "Some applications of Fourier series in the analytic theory of numbers." *Proc. Comb. Phil. Soc.*, **34** (1928).

Mordell, L. J., "Poisson's Summation Formula and the Riemann Zeta Function." *Jour. Lond. math. Soc.*, **4** (1929).

28. A More General Case

Let

$$f(s) = \sum_{n=1}^{\infty} \frac{a_n}{n^s} \qquad (28.1)$$

be a Dirichlet series expansion of an analytic function for $Re(s) > 1$, and suppose that the functional equation

$$f(1 - s) = g(s) f(s), \qquad (28.2)$$

provides an analytic continuation of $f(s)$ for $Re(s) < 1$.

Then the procedure outlined above yields a formal summation formula of the type

$$\sum_{n=1}^{\infty} a_n f(n) = R(f) + \sum_{n=1}^{\infty} a_n \int_{0}^{\infty} f(x) g(nx) \, dx, \qquad (28.3)$$

where

$$g(y) = \frac{1}{2\pi i} \int g(s) \, y^{s-1} \, ds, \qquad (28.4)$$

along an appropriate contour, and $R(f)$ represents residue terms depending upon f.

Comments and References

A discussion of this more general representation will be found in the paper by Ferrar referred to above. See also

Ferrar, W. L., "Summation formulae and their relations to Dirichlet series." *Compos. math.*, 1 (1935) 344.

The most famous formula of this type was used by Voronoi (Woronov) in his treatment of the sum $\Sigma_{n \leq N} \, d(n)$. Here $d(n)$, the Dirichlet divisor function, is the coefficient of n^{-s} in $\zeta^2(s)$,

$$\zeta^2(s) = \sum_{n=1}^{\infty} d(n) \, n^{-s}.$$

See

Voronoi, C., "Sur une fonction transcendante et ses applications à la summation de quelques séries." *Ann. sci. Éc. norm. sup.*, Paris, (3), **21** (1904) 207-267, 459.

For some interesting series connected with the Gauss circle function $r(n)$ and the transformation formula

$$t^{1/2} \sum_{n=0}^{\infty} r(n) \, e^{-n\pi t} = t^{-1/2} \sum_{n=0}^{\infty} r(n) \, e^{-n\pi/t},$$

see

Kochliakov, S., *Messeng. Math.*, **59** (1929) 1.

Further references will be found in the papers of Ferrar. A summary of recent results is given in

Sklar, A., "On some exact formulae in analytic number theory," *Report of the Institute in the Theory of Numbers.* Boulder, Colo.: Univ. of Colorado, June 21-July 17, 1959.

29.   Gaussian Sums

One of the beautiful applications of the transformation formula of the theta function is to the evaluation of the Gauss sum,

$$S(p, q) = \sum_{r=0}^{q-1} e^{-\pi i r^2 p/q}, \qquad (29.1)$$

where p and q are relatively prime integers. These sums are of great importance in number theory.

To find the connection between this sum and the theta functions, let us take the function

$$f(t) = \sum_{n=-\infty}^{\infty} e^{-n^2 t} = 1 + 2 \sum_{n=1}^{\infty} e^{-n^2 t}, \qquad (29.2)$$

and examine its behavior in the immediate neighborhood of the line of convergence, $Re(t) = 0$. Set $t = \epsilon + \pi i p/q$, where ϵ is a small positive quantity and p and q are relatively prime positive integers. Then

$$f(\epsilon + \pi i p/q) = 1 + 2 \sum_{n=1}^{\infty} e^{-n^2 \epsilon} e^{-\pi i n^2 p/q}$$

$$= 1 + 2 \sum_{r=1}^{q} e^{-\pi i r^2 p/q} \left[\sum_{s=0}^{\infty} e^{-(r+sq)^2 \epsilon} \right], \qquad (29.3)$$

upon taking account of the periodicity of $e^{-\pi i n^2 p/q}$ as a function of n.

The function of ϵ

$$\sum_{s=0}^{\infty} e^{-(r+sq)^2 \epsilon} \qquad (29.4)$$

behaves like the integral

$$\int_0^{\infty} e^{-(r+sq)^2 \epsilon} \, ds = \int_r^{\infty} e^{-w^2 \epsilon} \frac{dw}{q} \sim \frac{1}{q \sqrt{\epsilon}} \int_0^{\infty} e^{-w^2} \, dw = \frac{\sqrt{\pi}}{2q \sqrt{\epsilon}} \qquad (29.5)$$

as $\epsilon \to 0$.

Hence, asymptotically, as $\epsilon \to 0$, we have the equality

$$f\left(\epsilon + \frac{\pi i p}{q}\right) \sim \frac{\sqrt{\pi}}{q \sqrt{\epsilon}} S(p, q). \qquad (29.6)$$

The periodicity of $e^{-\pi i n^2 p/q}$ as a function of n enables us to write

$$S(p, q) = \sum_{r=0}^{q-1} = \sum_{r=1}^{q} .$$

We now employ the transformation formula

$$f(t) = \left(\frac{\pi}{t}\right)^{1/2} f\left(\frac{\pi^2}{t}\right) \tag{29.7}$$

and repeat the process with the function $f(\pi^2/t)$.

We have, for small ϵ,

$$\frac{\pi^2}{t} = \frac{\pi^2}{\epsilon + \pi i p/q} = \frac{\pi^2(\epsilon - \pi i p/q)}{\epsilon^2 + \pi^2 p^2/q^2} = \frac{\epsilon q^2}{p^2} - \frac{\pi i q}{p} + 0(\epsilon^2). \tag{29.8}$$

Hence, as above, as $\epsilon \to 0$,

$$f\left(\frac{\pi^2}{t}\right) \sim \frac{\sqrt{\pi}}{q\sqrt{\epsilon}} S(-q, p). \tag{29.9}$$

Observe that the effect of the transformation formula of the theta function has been to invert the roles of p and q.

Taking acount of the fact that

$$\left[\frac{\pi}{(\epsilon + \pi i p/q)}\right]^{1/2} \sim e^{-\pi i/4} \left(\frac{q}{p}\right)^{1/2} \tag{29.10}$$

as $\epsilon \to 0$, we see that as $\epsilon \to 0$,

$$\sqrt{\frac{\pi}{t}} f\left(\frac{\pi^2}{t}\right) \sim e^{-\pi i/4} \left(\frac{q}{p}\right)^{1/2} \left(\frac{\sqrt{\pi}}{q\sqrt{\epsilon}}\right) S(-q, p). \tag{29.11}$$

Hence, equating the two asymptotic equalities

$$\frac{1}{\sqrt{q}} \sum_{r=0}^{q-1} e^{-\pi i r^2 p/q} = \frac{e^{-\pi i/4}}{\sqrt{p}} \sum_{r=0}^{p-1} e^{\pi i r^2 q/p}, \tag{29.12}$$

a remarkable functional equation.

Comments and References

This result is due to Schaar. The result of Gauss,

$$\sum_{r=0}^{q-1} e^{2\pi i r^2/q} = \frac{(1 - i^q)}{(1 - i)} \sqrt{q},$$

valid for an odd integer q, is deduced by taking $p = 2$. The proof given above is due to Landsberg,

Landsberg, M., "Zur Theorie der Gauss'schen Summen und der linearen Trans-
formationen der Thetafunctionen." *Crelle's J. Mathematik,* **111** (1893).

For further history and a different method of proof, see

Lindelof, E., *Le Calcul des Residus.* . . . New York: Chelsea Publ. Co., 1947.

The simplest proof using contour integration is given by Mordell in his paper
in *Acta math.,* vol. 61. The precise reference is given at the end of Section 43.

See also

Lerch, M., "Zur Theorie der Gausschen Summen." *Math. Ann.* **57** (1903), 554.
Mordell, L. J., "On the reciprocity formula for the Gauss's sums in the quadratic
field." *Proc. Lond. math. Soc.,* **20** (1921-2), 289.

The Gauss sum is a particular trigonometric sum arising in the study of cyclotomic sums—sums of roots of unity occurring naturally in the problem of constructing a regular polygon of n sides by means of ruler and compass. It is interesting to see that this problem, extended to the lemniscate, led Gauss to his
independent discovery of elliptic functions.

30. Polya's Derivation

Let us now present a derivation of the fundamental transformation formula
of the theta function due to Polya which utilizes nothing more than the binomial
expansion and Stirling's asymptotic expansion for the factorial.

We start with the identity

$$(z^{1/2} + z^{-1/2})^{2m} = \sum_{v=-m}^{m} \binom{2m}{m+v} z^{v}. \tag{30.1}$$

Let $\omega = e^{2\pi i/l}$ be an lth root of unity. Then from 30.1 we derive the result

$$\sum_{-l/2 \leq v \leq l/2}' [(\omega^v z)^{1/2} + (\omega^v z)^{-1/2}]^{2m} = l \sum_{v=-[m/l]}^{[m/l]} \binom{2m}{m+lv} z^{lv}. \tag{30.2}$$

(Here and below $[y]$ denotes the greatest integer less than or equal to y).

Let s and t be fixed quantities, with s an arbitrary complex number and t a
real and positive quantity. Set

$$l = [(mt)^{1/2}], \qquad z = e^{s/l}. \tag{30.3}$$

Then, after division by 2^{2m}, the equation in 30.2 yields

$$\sum_{-l/2 \leq v \leq l/2} \left\{ \frac{1}{2} [e^{(s+2\pi i v)/l} + e^{-(s+2\pi i v)/l}] \right\}^{2m} \tag{30.4}$$

$$= \sum_{-l/2 \leq v \leq l/2} \left\{ 1 + \frac{s + 2\pi i v}{8 l^2} + \cdots \right\}^{8 l^2 (m/4 l^2)}$$

$$= \sum_{v=-[m/l]}^{[m/l]} \frac{[(tm)^{1/2}]}{2^{2m}} \binom{2m}{m + [(tm)^{1/2}]v} e^{sv}. \tag{30.4}$$

We now wish to let l approach infinity and use the following two limit theorems.

(a) $\displaystyle\lim_{n\to\infty} \left(1 + \frac{x_n}{n}\right)^n = e^x$ if $\displaystyle\lim_{n\to\infty} x_n = x,$

(b) $\displaystyle\lim_{n\to\infty} \frac{n^{1/2}}{2^{2n}} \binom{2n}{n+r} = \frac{e^{-x^2}}{\pi^{1/2}}$ if $\displaystyle\lim_{n\to\infty} \frac{r}{\sqrt{n}} = x,$ (30.5)

where n and r are positive integers.

The equation in 30.4 yields in the limit

$$\sum_{v=-\infty}^{\infty} e^{(s+2\pi i v)^2/4t} = \left(\frac{t}{\pi}\right)^{1/2} \sum_{v=-\infty}^{\infty} e^{-tv^2+sv}, \qquad (30.6)$$

the desired theta function transformation, given in Section 9.

Comments and References

For additional details required to justify the limiting processes we refer the reader to Polya's paper,

Polya, G., "Elementarer Beweis einer Thetaformel." *Sitz. der Phys.-Math. Klasse.* Berlin (1927) 158-161.

Although the foregoing result at first may seem like a tour de force, in actuality it is closely connected with the fact that the continuous diffusion process may be considered to be a limit of a discrete random walk process. Since the random walk is ruled by the binomial expansion, and the diffusion process by the heat equation which gives rise to the Gaussian distribution, we see that it is not at all surprising that a modification of binomial expansions should yield the theta function formula.

31. Discussion

This brings us to the end of the first part of the monograph, devoted to the proof of the transformation formula for the theta function and related topics. The second part will be devoted to results of quite different nature, established by the use of a variety of methods.

32. A Fundamental Infinite Product

Let us begin our foray into a different area with the consideration of the expression of $\theta_4(z)$ as an infinite product. From this result some interesting infinite series can be obtained.

Theorem 6:

$$\theta_4(z) = \prod_{n=1}^{\infty} (1 - 2q^{2n-1} \cos 2z + q^{4n-2}) \prod_{n=1}^{\infty} (1 - q^{2n}). \qquad (32.1)$$

There are no simple proofs known of the complete result, but there are a number of fairly straightforward ways of deriving the partial result

$$\theta_4(z) = k \prod_{n=1}^{\infty} (1 - 2q^{2n-1} \cos 2z + q^{4n-2}), \qquad (32.2)$$

where k is independent of z. We shall content ourselves with this result, since with it we can obtain a number of subsidiary identities.

We shall rely upon contour integration to a great extent, and also upon certain types of functional equations introduced by Euler.

Comments and References

For derivations of the value of k, see Whittaker and Watson, where two methods may be found, and the chapter in Hardy and Wright. Perhaps the easiest proof is contained in

Lenz, H., "Eine Bemerkung zur Einführung der Theta-funktionen." *Jber. dtsch. Mat. Ver.*, **58** (1956) Abt. 2, 57.

33. Zeroes

The form of $\theta_1(z)$ makes it evident that $z = 0$ is a zero of $\theta_1(z)$, whence $\pi/2$, $\pi/2 + \pi t/2$, and $\pi t/2$ are, respectively, zeroes of the functions $\theta_2(z)$, $\theta_3(z)$, and $\theta_4(z)$. The functional equations of Section 3 show that $z_0 + m\pi + n\pi t$ is a zero of a theta function whenever z_0 is. Are there any zeroes other those we have obtained in this obvious fashion ?

Let us show that in any parallelogram with corners t_0, $t_0 + \pi$, $t_0 + \pi + \pi t$, $t_0 + \pi t$, there is exactly one zero, a result which shows that we have indeed all of the zeroes of the theta functions. Moreover, the method is important, since we shall employ a more sophisticated version of it in a moment to obtain an elegant Fourier series expansion.

Consider the integral

$$N = \frac{1}{2\pi i} \int_P \frac{\theta'(z)}{\theta(z)} \, dz, \qquad (33.1)$$

taken around the parallelogram described immediately above. As we know, this expression is equal to the number of zeroes of $\theta(z)$ lying inside P.

Writing out the contour integral explicitly, we have

$$N = \frac{1}{2\pi i} \int_{t_0}^{t_0+\pi} \left[\frac{\theta'(z)}{\theta(z)} - \frac{\theta'(z + \pi t)}{\theta(z + \pi t)} \right] dz$$

$$- \frac{1}{2\pi i} \int_{t_0}^{t_0+\pi t} \left[\frac{\theta'(z)}{\theta(z)} - \frac{\theta'(z + \pi)}{\theta(z + \pi)} \right] dz. \qquad (33.2)$$

The functional equations of Section 3 readily yield the identities

$$\frac{\theta'(z + \pi)}{\theta(z + \pi)} = \frac{\theta'(z)}{\theta(z)}, \qquad \frac{\theta'(z + \pi t)}{\theta(z + \pi t)} = -2i + \frac{\theta'(z)}{\theta(z)}, \qquad (33.3)$$

upon taking logarithmic derivatives. Using these relations, we see that 33.2 reduces quite simply to

$$N = \frac{1}{2\pi i} \int_{t_0}^{t_0+\pi} 2i \, dz = 1. \qquad (33.4)$$

This establishes the desired result.

34.　Proof of Theorem 6

With these preliminaries disposed of, we are ready to establish the weaker statement of 32.2. Consider the infinite product.

$$f(z) = \prod_{n=1}^{\infty} (1 - 2q^{2n-1} \cos 2z + q^{4n-2})$$

$$= \prod_{n=1}^{\infty} (1 - q^{2n-1}e^{2iz}) \prod_{n=1}^{\infty} (1 - q^{2n-1}e^{-2iz}). \qquad (34.1)$$

The absolute convergence of the series $\Sigma_n \, q^{2n-1}$ permits us to conclude that $f(z)$ is an analytic function of z throughout the finite z plane. It is clear that $f(z + \pi) = f(z)$, and we see that

$$f(z + \pi t) = \prod_{n=1}^{\infty} (1 - q^{2n+1}e^{2iz}) \prod_{n=1}^{\infty} (1 - q^{2n-1}e^{-2iz})$$

$$= f(z) (1 - qe^{2iz})^{-1} (1 - q^{-1}e^{-2iz})$$

$$= - q^{-1}e^{-2iz} f(z). \qquad (34.2)$$

The zeroes of $f(z)$ are easily seen to be simple zeroes at the points where $1 - q^{2n-1}e^{\pm 2iz} = 0$, which is to say at the points

$$2iz = (2n + 1) \pi t + 2m\pi i, \qquad m, n = 0, \pm 1, \pm 2, \dots. \qquad (34.3)$$

Hence $\theta_4(z)/f(z)$ is a doubly-periodic function of z with no zeroes or poles, and thus, invoking Liouville's theorem, a constant. This establishes the equation in 32.2.

Comments and References

So far, we have been following Whittaker and Watson.

35. An Infinite Series for $\theta_4'(z)/\theta_4(z)$

We have bypassed the problem of the determination of k since we do not need it for the derivation of some interesting infinite series for the logarithmic derivative of $\theta_4(z)$. From 32.2 we obtain the expression

$$\log \theta_4(z) = \sum_{n=1}^{\infty} \log (1 - q^{2n-1}e^{2iz}) + \sum_{n=1}^{\infty} \log (1 - q^{2n-1}e^{-2iz}) + \log k, \quad (35.1)$$

which, upon differentiation, yields

$$\frac{\theta_4'(z)}{\theta_4(z)} = \sum_{n=1}^{\infty} \frac{-2iq^{2n-1}e^{2iz}}{1 - q^{2n-1}e^{2iz}} + \sum_{n=1}^{\infty} \frac{2iq^{2n-1}e^{-2iz}}{1 - q^{2n-1}e^{-2iz}}, \quad (35.2)$$

or, grouping terms,

$$\frac{\theta_4'(z)}{\theta_4(z)} = \sum_{n=1}^{\infty} \frac{q^{2n-1} \sin 2z}{1 - 2q^{2n-1} \cos 2z + q^{4n-2}}. \quad (35.3)$$

36. A More Interesting Series

To obtain a more elegant representation for $\theta_4'(z)/\theta_4(z)$, of a type that plays an important role in analytic number theory, we revert to 35.2 and write

$$\frac{q^{2n-1}e^{2iz}}{1 - q^{2n-1}e^{2iz}} = \sum_{m=1}^{\infty} q^{(2n-1)m}e^{+2miz},$$

$$\frac{q^{2n-1}e^{-2iz}}{1 - q^{2n-1}e^{-2iz}} = \sum_{m=1}^{\infty} q^{(2n-1)m}e^{-2miz}. \quad (36.1)$$

Interchanging the orders of summation, we have

$$\frac{\theta_4'(z)}{\theta_4(z)} = -2i \sum_{m=1}^{\infty}\sum_{n=1}^{\infty} q^{(2n-1)m}e^{2miz} + 2i \sum_{m=1}^{\infty}\sum_{n=1}^{\infty} q^{(2n-1)m}e^{-2miz}$$

$$= \sum_{m=1}^{\infty} \left[2ie^{-2miz} - 2ie^{2miz} \right] \left[\sum_{n=1}^{\infty} q^{(2n-1)m} \right]$$

$$= \sum_{m=1}^{\infty} \frac{4q^m \sin 2mz}{1 - q^{2m}} . \tag{36.2}$$

We thus have a Fourier expansion for $\theta_4'(z)/\theta_4(z)$ valid in the region $|\,Im(z)\,| < Im(\pi t)/2$. This restriction is necessary if we wish the series in 36.1 to converge.

37.   Hermite's Derivation

Let us now present an elegant technique used by Hermite to derive 36.2 and similar relations. Given the expansion

$$\frac{\theta_4'(z)}{\theta_4(z)} = \sum_{n=1}^{\infty} a_n \sin 2nz, \tag{37.1}$$

the Fourier coefficients a_n are determined by the relation

$$a_n = \frac{2}{\pi} \int_{-\pi/2}^{\pi/2} \frac{\theta_4'(z)}{\theta_4(z)} \sin 2nz \, dz. \tag{37.2}$$

To evaluate this integral we begin with the contour integral

$$\int_P \frac{\theta_4'(z)}{\theta_4(z)} e^{2niz} \, dz, \tag{37.3}$$

taken around the parallelogram whose corners are $-\pi/2$, $\pi/2$, $\pi/2 + \pi t$, $-\pi/2 + \pi t$, where n is a positive integer. Proceeding as in Section 33, we readily see that

$$\int_{-\pi/2}^{\pi/2} \frac{\theta_4'(z)}{\theta_4(z)} e^{2niz} \, dz = \frac{2\pi i q^n}{1 - q^{2n}} . \tag{37.4}$$

Since $\theta_4'(z)/\theta_4(z)$ is an odd function, this relation reduces to

$$\int_{-\pi/2}^{\pi/2} \frac{\theta_4'(z)}{\theta_4(z)} \sin 2nz \, dz = \frac{2\pi q^n}{1 - q^{2n}} , \tag{37.5}$$

from which we deduce the series of 36.2.

Similarly, it can be shown that

$$\frac{\theta_1'(z)}{\theta_1(z)} = \cot z + 4 \sum_{n=1}^{\infty} \frac{q^{2n} \sin 2nz}{1 - q^{2n}} ,$$

$$\frac{\theta_2'(z)}{\theta_2(z)} = -\tan z + 4\sum_{n=1}^{\infty} \frac{(-1)^n q^{2n} \sin 2nz}{1 - q^{2n}},$$

$$\frac{\theta_3'(z)}{\theta_3(z)} = 4\sum_{n=1}^{\infty} \frac{(-1)^n q^n \sin 2nz}{1 - q^{2n}}. \tag{37.6}$$

38. Some Results of Watson

Some interesting expansions due to Watson which can be established as above by use of Liouville's theorem are

$$\frac{\theta_2\theta_3(z)\,\theta_4(z)}{\theta_1(z)} = -2i\sum_{n=-\infty}^{\infty} \frac{q^{n^2}e^{2niz}}{q^{-n}e^{-iz} - q^n e^{iz}}, \tag{38.1}$$

$$\frac{\theta_2\theta_3(z)\,\theta_4(z)}{\theta_2(z)} = 2\sum_{n=-\infty}^{\infty} \frac{(-1)^n q^{n^2}e^{2niz}}{q^{-n}e^{-iz} + q^n e^{iz}}, \tag{38.2}$$

$$\frac{\theta_2\theta_1(z)\,\theta_2(z)}{\theta_3(z)} = -2i\sum_{n=-\infty}^{\infty} \frac{(-1)^n q^{[n+(1/2)]^2}e^{(2n+1)iz}}{q^{-n-(1/2)}e^{-iz} + q^{n+(1/2)}e^{iz}}, \tag{38.3}$$

$$\frac{\theta_2\theta_1(z)\,\theta_2(z)}{\theta_4(z)} = -2i\sum_{n=-\infty}^{\infty} \frac{q^{[n+(1/2)]^2}e^{(2n+1)iz}}{q^{-n(-1/2)}e^{-iz} - q^{n(+1/2)}e^{iz}}, \tag{38.4}$$

$$\frac{\theta_3\theta_2(z)\,\theta_4(z)}{\theta_1(z)} = -i\sum_{n=-\infty}^{\infty} q^{n^2}e^{2niz}\left(\frac{1+q^{2n}e^{2iz}}{1-q^{2n}e^{2iz}}\right), \tag{38.5}$$

$$\frac{\theta_3\theta_1(z)\,\theta_3(z)}{\theta_2(z)} = i\sum_{n=-\infty}^{\infty} (-1)^n q^{n^2}e^{2niz}\left(\frac{1-q^{2n}e^{2iz}}{1+q^{2n}e^{2iz}}\right), \tag{38.6}$$

$$\frac{\theta_3\theta_2(z)\,\theta_4(z)}{\theta_3(z)} = \sum_{n=-\infty}^{\infty} (-1)^n q^{[n+(1/2)]^2}e^{(2n+1)iz}\left(\frac{1-q^{2n+1}e^{2iz}}{1+q^{2n+1}e^{2iz}}\right), \tag{38.7}$$

$$\frac{\theta_3\theta_1(z)\,\theta_3(z)}{\theta_4(z)} = -i\sum_{n=-\infty}^{\infty} q^{[n+(1/2)]^2}e^{(2n+1)iz}\left(\frac{1+q^{2n+1}e^{2iz}}{1-q^{2n+1}e^{2iz}}\right), \tag{38.8}$$

$$\frac{\theta_4\theta_2(z)\,\theta_3(z)}{\theta_1(z)} = -i\sum_{n=-\infty}^{\infty} (-1)^n q^{n^2}e^{2niz}\left(\frac{1+q^{2n}e^{2iz}}{1-q^{2n}e^{2iz}}\right), \tag{38.9}$$

$$\frac{\theta_4\theta_1(z)\,\theta_4(z)}{\theta_2(z)} = i\sum_{n=-\infty}^{\infty} q^{n^2}e^{2niz}\left(\frac{1-q^{2n}e^{2iz}}{1+q^{2n}e^{2iz}}\right), \tag{38.10}$$

$$\frac{\theta_4\theta_1(z)\,\theta_4(z)}{\theta_3(z)} = -i\sum_{n=-\infty}^{\infty} q^{[n+(1/2)]^2}e^{(2n+1)iz}\left(\frac{1-q^{2n+1}e^{2iz}}{1+q^{2n+1}e^{2iz}}\right), \tag{38.11}$$

$$\frac{\theta_4 \theta_2(z)\, \theta_3(z)}{\theta_4(z)} = \sum_{n=-\infty}^{\infty} (-1)^n q^{[n+(1/2)]^2} e^{(2n+1)iz} \left(\frac{1 + q^{2n+1} e^{2iz}}{1 - q^{2n+1} e^{2iz}} \right). \qquad (38.12)$$

The symbols θ_1, θ_2, θ_3, and θ_4 here represent the quantities $\theta_1(0)$, $\theta_2(0)$, $\theta_3(0)$, $\theta_4(0)$.

Comments and References

Watson, G. N., "Generating functions of class-numbers." *Compos. math.*, **1** 1935) 39.

These are related to results given by Hermite:

Hermite, C., *Œuvres*, vol. 2, p. 244, 1908.

Many other fascinating expansions of this type may be found in Whittaker and Watson and in other standard works on elliptic functions. We have presented the foregoing to give the reader some idea of the results that are available and the methods that exist.

As pointed out by Mordell, relations of this nature are readily verified by means of functional equation techniques of the type used in Section 50.

39. Eulerian Results

If, in 32.1, we set $z = 0$, we obtain

$$\theta_4(0) = \prod_{n=1}^{\infty} (1 - q^{2n-1})^2 \prod_{n=1}^{\infty} (1 - q^{2n}), \qquad (39.1)$$

or

$$1 - 2q + 2q^4 - 2q^9 + \dots = \prod_{n=1}^{\infty} (1 - q^{2n-1})^2 \prod_{n=1}^{\infty} (1 - q^{2n}). \qquad (39.2)$$

Similarly, if we set $\cos 2z = 0$, say $z = \pi/4$, we have

$$1 - 2q^4 + 2q^{16} - \dots = \prod_{n=1}^{\infty} (1 + q^{4n-2}) \prod_{n=1}^{\infty} (1 - q^{2n}). \qquad (39.3)$$

These results are quite startling and unbelievable at first glance. Some of the many results of this type can be derived using simple methods, some can be obtained readily using the theory of elliptic functions, while others require the full power of generalized basic hypergeometric functions together with considerable ingenuity and patience.

Following Ramanujan, we shall call such expansions *Eulerian*, since Euler was the first to obtain identities of this nature. He obtained the famous result

$$(1 - x)(1 - x^2)(1 - x^3) \dots = \sum_{n=-\infty}^{\infty} (-1)^n x^{n(3n+1)/2}, \qquad (39.4)$$

and the expansions

$$\prod_{k=1}^{\infty} (1 - x^k t) = \sum_{n=0}^{\infty} \frac{(-1)^n x^{n(n+1)/2} t^n}{\prod_{k=1}^{n} (1 - x^k)},$$

$$\prod_{k=1}^{\infty} (1 - x^k t)^{-1} = \sum_{n=0}^{\infty} \frac{t^n}{(1 - x)(1 - x^2) \dots (1 - x^n)}, \qquad (39.5)$$

as well as a number of other results.

We leave to the reader the challenge of deriving 39.4 using the foregoing relations concerning theta functions, and we turn to the derivation of those in 39.5.

Comments and References

There is a singular beauty about such relations as 39.2, 39.3, and 39.5. Let us quote the words of G. N. Watson on this theme:

"The study of Ramanujan's work and of the problems to which it gives rise inevitably recalls to mind Lamé's remark that, when reading Hermite's papers on modular functions, 'on a la chair de poule.' I would express my own attitude with more prolixity by saying that such a formula as

$$\int_0^{\infty} e^{-3\pi x^2} \frac{\sin h \, \pi x \, dx}{\sin h \, 3\pi x}$$

$$= \frac{1}{e^{2\pi/3} \sqrt{3}} \sum_{n=0}^{\infty} \frac{e^{-2n(n+1)\pi}}{(1 + e^{-\pi})^2 (1 + e^{-3\pi})^2 \dots [1 + e^{-(2n+1)\pi}]^2}$$

gives me a thrill which is indistinguishable from the thrill which I feel when I enter the Sagrestia Nuova of the Capella Medici and see before me the austere beauty of the four statues representing 'Day,' 'Night,' 'Evening,' and 'Dawn,' which Michelangelo has set over the tomb of Giuliano de' Medici and Lorenzo de' Medici."

p. 80 of Watson, G. N., "The final problem: an account of the mock theta-functions." *Lond. math. Soc.*, **XI** (1936) 55.

The two masters of this domain of analysis were Jacobi and Ramanujan. For an account of some of Ramanujan's results, see

Hardy, G. H., *Ramanujan*. Cambridge: Cambridge Univ. Press, 1940, and Mordell, L. J., "Ramanujan," *Nature*, **148** (1941), pp. 642-647.

For results concerning hypergeometric series and many further references, see

Bailey, W. N., *Generalized Hypergeometric Series*. Cambridge: Cambridge Univ. Press, 1935.

The first paper devoted to basic hypergeometric series is

Heine, E., "Über die Reihe $1 + \frac{(q^a - 1)(q^b - 1)}{(q - 1)(q^c - 1)} z + \dots$, *J. für Math.*, **32** (1846) 210; *ibid.*, **34** (1847) 285.

———, *Handbuch der Kugelfunctionen*, vol. 1. Berlin: 1878.

Since then, a number of papers have been devoted to their study. For the associated continued fractions, see

Perron, O., *Die Lehre von den Kettenbruchen*, vol. 2. Teubner, 1957.

The usual hypergeometric function of Gauss is the limit of the basic hypergeometric function as $q \to 1$.

Results of the foregoing type—39.1, 39.2, and 39.3—may also be derived from combinatorial considerations; see

Hardy, G. H., and Wright, E. M., *Introduction to the Theory of Numbers*. Oxford: Oxford Univ. Press, 1945.

McMahon, P. A., *Combinatory Analysis*, vol. I, 1915, and vol. II. Cambridge: Cambridge Univ. Press, 1916.

Some of the history of these results and further references may be found in this latter reference.

40. Euler's Formulas and Functional Equations

Let us now turn to the derivation of the first formula in 39.5. Write

$$f(x, t) = \prod_{k=1}^{\infty} (1 - x^k t). \tag{40.1}$$

Then it is easily seen that

$$f(x, t) = (1 - xt) f(x, tx). \tag{40.2}$$

Writing

$$f(x, t) = \sum_{n=0}^{\infty} a_n(x) t^n, \tag{40.3}$$

the functional equation in 40.3 yields

$$\sum_{n=0}^{\infty} a_n(x) \, t^n = (1 - xt) \sum_{n=0}^{\infty} a_n(x) \, x^n t^n, \tag{40.4}$$

or

$$a_n(x) = a_n(x) \, x^n - a_{n-1}(x) \, x^n. \tag{40.5}$$

From this we readily obtain the desired result:

$$a_n(x) = \frac{(-1)^n x^{n(n+1)/2}}{\displaystyle\prod_{k=1}^{n} (1 - x^k)}. \tag{40.6}$$

The second formula is established in similar fashion.

Comments and References

Two interesting related results are due to Shanks:

$$\sum_{s=0}^{n-1} \frac{P_n x^{s(2n+1)}}{P_s} = \sum_{s=1}^{2n} x^{s(s-1)/2},$$

$$\sum_{s=1}^{n} \frac{P_n x^{s(2n+1)}}{P_s} = \sum_{s=1}^{2n+1} x^{s(s-1)/2},$$

where

$$P_n = \prod_{s=1}^{n} \left(\frac{1 - x^{2s}}{1 - x^{2s-1}} \right).$$

From these, he derives the known identity of Gauss:

$$\prod_{n=1}^{\infty} \left(\frac{1 - x^{2n}}{1 - x^{2n-1}} \right) = \sum_{1}^{\infty} x^{n(n-1)/2},$$

and the evaluation of Gauss' sum. See

Shanks, D., "Two theorems of Gauss." *Pacific J. Math.*, **8** (1958) 609.

Other applications of this technique due to Euler will be found in Hardy and Wright.

41.   Partial Fractions

Another approach is the following. Consider the function

$$f_N(z) = \prod_{k=1}^{N} (1 - x^k z)^{-1}. \tag{41.1}$$

Then, using a partial fraction decomposition, we have

$$f_N(z) = \sum_{k=1}^{N} \frac{a_k(x)}{1 - x^k z}, \tag{41.2}$$

where

$$a_K(x) = \lim_{z \to x^{-K}} (1 - x^K z) f_N(z)$$

$$= \prod_{k=1}^{K-1} (1 - x^{k-K}) \prod_{k=K+1}^{N} (1 - x^{k-K})^{-1}.$$

Thus

$$a_K(x) = \prod_{k=1}^{K-1} (1 - x^{-k})^{-1} \prod_{k=1}^{N-K} (1 - x^k)^{-1}. \tag{41.4}$$

Letting $N \to \infty$, we obtain the result

$$\frac{\prod\limits_{k=1}^{\infty} (1 - x^k)}{\prod\limits_{k=1}^{\infty} (1 - x^k z)} = \sum_{K=1}^{\infty} \frac{\prod\limits_{k=1}^{K-1} (1 - x^{-k})^{-1}}{(1 - x^K z)} . \tag{41.5}$$

Setting $z = 0$, we obtain the first formula of 39.5 for $t = 1$. We do not, however, seem to obtain the second formula in this way.

Comments and References

An advantage of the technique of partial fractions is that the same procedure can be used to derive analogous expressions for the function

$$f(z) = \prod_{k,l=1}^{\infty} (1 - x^k y^l z)^{-1}.$$

Thus

$$\frac{\prod\limits_{k,l=1}^{\infty} (1 - x^k y^l)}{\prod\limits_{k,l=1}^{\infty} (1 - x^k y^l z)} = \sum_{k,l=1}^{\infty} \frac{b_k}{(1 - x^k y^l z)},$$

where

$$b_{KL} = \prod_{k,l=1}^{K-1,L-1} (1 - x^k y^{-l})^{-1} \prod_{k=1}^{\infty} \prod_{l=0}^{L-1} (1 - x^k y^{-l})^{-1} \prod_{k=0}^{K-1} \prod_{l=1}^{\infty} (1 - x^{-k} y^l).$$

See

Bellman, R., "The expansions of some infinite products." *Duke math. J.*, **24** (1957) 353.

Some other references will be found there. Infinite products of the foregoing form play an important part in statistical mechanics.

42. Mock Theta Functions

The last years of Ramanujan's life were devoted to the study of a class of functions called *mock theta functions*. Typical of such functions are

$$f(q) = \sum_{n=0}^{\infty} \frac{q^{n^2}}{(1 + q)^2 (1 + q^2)^2 \cdots (1 + q^n)^2}, \tag{42.1}$$

$$\phi(q) = \sum_{n=0}^{\infty} \frac{q^{n^2}}{(1 + q)^2 (1 + q^4) \cdots (1 + q^{2n})} . \tag{42.2}$$

These are related to the theta functions not only in form, but also through certain integrals of Mordell we shall meet below, in Section 43.

Comments and References

See

Watson, G. N., "The final problem: an account of the mock theta-functions." *J. Lond. math. Soc.*, **XI** (1936) 55.
Dragonette, L. A., "Some asymptotic formulae for the mock theta series of Ramanujan." *Trans. Amer. math. Soc.*, **72** (1952) 474.

For functions related in form, but of less significance in the general theory—the "fake" theta functions—see

Rogers, L. J., *Proc. Lond. math. Soc.*, (2), **16** (1917) 315.

and for another class of related functions, see

Basoco, M. A., "On certain arithmetical functions due to G. Humbert." *J. Math. pures appl.*, **9** (1947) 237.

43. The Mordell Integral

The contour integral

$$\phi(\tau, u) = \int \frac{e^{\pi i \tau x^2 + 2\pi i u x}}{e^{2\pi i x} - 1} \, dx \tag{43.1}$$

is intimately connected with theta functions and mock theta functions on one hand and with the Riemann zeta function on the other.

A special class of integrals of this nature was introduced by Riemann to study the asymptotic behavior of $\zeta(\frac{1}{2} + it)$ as $t \to \infty$, and, presumably, the Riemann hypothesis is based upon the form of the asymptotic relation he derived. Riemann also derived another proof of the functional equation for $\zeta(s)$ by means of this integral. Although Riemann's results were never published, some notes he left were fortunately competed and polished by Siegel.

An integral of this type was used by Kronecker to derive the reciprocity relation for the Gauss sums, and particular versions of it appear in the work by Watson on mock theta functions cited above, and in various papers of Ramanujan, Lerch, and Van der Corput. Mordell studied the general integral in great detail, using both functional equation techniques and contour integration, and derived a large number of interesting results, including as a by-product a very simple proof of the reciprocity formula for Gauss sums.

Comments and References

See

Siegel, C. L., "Über Riemanns Nachlass zur analytischen Zahlentheorie, *Quellen und Studien zur Geschichte der Mathematik.*" *Astronomie und Physik*, band 2, pp. 45-80, 1933.

As Siegel points out, the asymptotic formula of Riemann contains as a special case the "approximate functional equation" for $\zeta(s)$ of Hardy and Littlewood. For a discussion of these matters, see

Titchmarsh, E. C., *The Zeta-function of Riemann.* Cambridge: Cambridge Univ. Press, 1930.

For an evaluation of the Gauss sum by means of contour integration, see

Kronecker, L., "Summierung der Gaussschen Reihen $\Sigma_{h=0}^{r-1} e^{2\pi i h^2/n}$." *J. reine angew. Math.*, **105** (1889) 267; *ibid.*, 345.

The paper by Mordell, which contains extensive references to work by Ramanujan, Mordell himself, and others, is

Mordell, L. J., "The definite integral $\int_{-\infty}^{\infty} e^{ax^2+bx} dx/(e^{cx} + d)$ and the analytic theory of numbers." *Acta math.*, Stock. **61** (1933) 323.

His results were originally published in the *Quarterly Journal of Mathematics*, in 1918.

44. Some New Types of Relations

So far we have restricted our attention to expansions of various types valid for individual theta functions. Let us now turn to a discussion of the many relations that connect the various theta functions. All of the relations that appear below may be found in Jacobi's magnum opus or, more conveniently, in Whittaker and Watson, based upon use of Liouville's theorem. Since we plan to present another type of proof a little farther on, distinct from that of Jacobi or from the standard complex variables method, this presentation will be quite sketchy.

45. Relations Connecting Squares of Theta Functions

Let us begin with the following result.

Theorem 7:

$$\theta_2^2(z)\theta_4^2 = \theta_4^2(z)\theta_2^2 - \theta_1^2(z)\theta_3^2.$$

Here, and in what follows, $\theta_2 = \theta_2(0)$, $\theta_3 = \theta_3(0)$, $\theta_4 = \theta_4(0)$.

Although the proof we given immediately below is a verification, subsequently, we shall present a derivation. Consider the function

$$f(z) = \frac{\theta_4^2(z)\theta_2^2 - \theta_1^2(z)\theta_3^2}{\theta_2^2(z)}. \tag{45.2}$$

It is easily verified that $f(z)$ is a doubly-periodic function with no poles and hence must be a constant. To determine the constant, we choose a convenient value for z such as $z = \pi t/2$.

Similarly, one can establish

$$\theta_4^2(z)\theta_4^2 = \theta_3^2(z)\theta_3^2 - \theta_2^2(z)\theta_2^2, \tag{45.3}$$

which for $z = 0$ yields the famous identity

$$\theta_4^4 + \theta_2^4 = \theta_3^4. \tag{45.4}$$

Comments and References

The original results of Jacobi were given in

Jacobi, C. G., *Fundamenta Nova Theoriae Functionum Ellipticarum.* Konigsberg: Ges. Werke, I, 1829. pp. 497-538.

A very simple and elegant proof of 45.4 requiring no knowledge of the theory of elliptic or theta functions, is given in

Van der Pol, B., "Demonstration élémentaire de la relation $\theta_3^4 = \theta_0^4 + \theta_2^4 \ldots$" *Enseign. math.*, (2), **1** (1956) 258.

The method of Van der Pol is a particular example of the powerful method developed by Liouville and brought to a peak of perfection by Bell. See

Bell, E. T., *Algebraic Arithmetic*, vol. VII. New York: Amer. math. Soc. (Colloqia), 1927

In this book will be found a fascinating amalgam of algebra and analysis, connecting one-dimensional and multidimensional theta functions and the theory of numbers. Many other results will be found in earlier papers of Bell.

46. Addition Formulae

In similar fashion, we can establish results of the following nature.

Theorem 8:

$$\theta_3(z+y)\,\theta_3(z-y)\,\theta_3^2 = \theta_3^2(y)\,\theta_3^2(z) + \theta_1^2(y)\,\theta_1^2(z). \tag{46.1}$$

A special case of this is the duplication formula

$$\theta_3(2z)\theta_3^3 = \theta_3^4(z) + \theta_1^4(z). \tag{46.2}$$

Comments and References

Many more complicated results involving linear combinations of the variables were given by Jacobi (see Whittaker and Watson). Further results can be obtained in the same way.

47. Landen's Formula

A result of great historical interest and computational importance may be expressed in the following concise form.

Theorem 9:

$$\frac{\theta_3(z, t)\, \theta_4(z, t)}{\theta_4(2z, 2t)} = \frac{\theta_3(0, t)\, \theta_4(0, t)}{\theta_4(0, 2t)}. \tag{47.1}$$

Comments and References

Let a and b be two positive numbers, and let two sequences $\{a_n\}$ and $\{b_n\}$ be determined by the recurrence relations

$$a_{n+1} = \frac{a_n + b_n}{2}, \qquad b_{n+1} = \sqrt{a_n b_n}, \qquad n \geq 0, \tag{47.1a}$$

where $a_0 = a_0 \; b_0 = b$. It is easy to show that a_n and b_n converge to a common limit, $M(a, b)$, which is known as the *arithmetic-geometric mean* of Gauss.

The importance of this transformation is twofold. In the first place, Gauss showed by means of a Landen transformation that

$$\int_0^{\pi/2} \frac{d\theta}{(a_1^2 \cos^2 \theta + b_1^2 \sin^2 \theta)^{1/2}} = \int_0^{\pi/2} \frac{d\theta}{(a^2 \cos^2 \theta + b^2 \sin^2 \theta)^{1/2}}, \tag{47.1b}$$

a result which yields, upon repeated application, the relation

$$\int_0^{\pi/2} \frac{d\theta}{(a^2 \cos^2 \theta + b^2 \sin^2 \theta)^{1/2}} = \frac{\pi/2}{M(a,b)}. \tag{47.1c}$$

Secondly, Gauss showed that the theory of elliptic functions can be founded on the function $M(a, b)$.

For a discussion of these matters, see

Watson, G. N., "The Marquis and the Land Agent, a Tale of the Eighteenth Century." *Math. Gaz.*, **XVII** (1933) 5.
Gauss, C. F., *Werke*, vol. III, p. 352.
Whittaker, E. T. and Watson, G. N., *A Course of Modern Analysis*, chap. XII, p. 533, exer. 46. Cambridge: Cambridge Univ. Press, 1935.

There are generalizations of the identity of 47.1c, valid for hyperelliptic integrals, but none of the same elegance.

48. The Fundamental Transformation Formula

Finally, we leave it as an exercise for the reader to show that the basic transformation formula, which was used as a backdrop for so many different techniques of analysis in the first part of this monograph, can also be established by use of Liouville's theorem.

49.   Some Results of Schottky

Let us now, following Schottky, combine the foregoing results concerning products of theta functions with some simple aspects of the theory of differential equations.

As we know, each of the four theta functions satisfies the linear parabolic partial differential equation

$$\frac{\partial^2 u}{\partial z^2} = -\frac{4}{\pi i}\frac{\partial u}{\partial t}, \tag{49.1}$$

the one-dimensional heat, or diffusion, equation. From the constancy of the coefficients, we may conclude that if $u(z) = u(z, t)$ is a solution, then $u(z + w)$ is a solution for any value of w. Consider then the product of any two theta functions,

$$h(z, t) = u_1(z + w)\, u_2(z - w). \tag{49.2}$$

We assert that h satisfies the partial differential equation

$$h_{zz} + h_{ww} = -\frac{8}{\pi i}\, h_t. \tag{49.3}$$

This fact follows readily from the formulae

$$h_{zz} = u_2(z - w)\frac{\partial^2}{\partial z^2}u_1(z + w) + u_1(z + w)\frac{\partial^2 u_2}{\partial z^2}(z - w)$$

$$+ 2\frac{\partial u_1}{\partial z}(z + w)\frac{\partial u_2}{\partial z}(z - w),$$

$$h_{ww} = u_2(z - w)\frac{\partial^2}{\partial z^2}u_1(z + w) + u_1(z + w)\frac{\partial^2 u_2}{\partial z^2}(z - w)$$

$$- 2\frac{\partial u_1}{\partial z}(z + w)\frac{\partial u_2}{\partial z}(z - w). \tag{49.4}$$

Let u_1, u_2, u_3, and u_4 denote the four theta functions, taken in any order. As we have just seen, there exist relations of the type

$$u_1(z + w)\, u_2(z - w) = a_1 u_1(z)\, u_2(z) + b_1 u_3(z)\, u_4(z), \tag{49.5}$$

where the coefficients a_1 and b_1 are functions of w. In particular, if we let $F(z)$ be the product of any two even theta functions and $G(z)$ be the product of any even theta functions by an odd theta function, we may write

$$F(0)\, u_1(z + w)\, u_2(z - w) = F(z)\, F(w) \pm G(z)\, G(w). \tag{49.6}$$

The sign $\pm$ changes if we interchange u_1 and u_2. To normalize this, write

$$f(z) = \frac{F(z)}{F(0)^{1/2}}, \qquad g(w) = \frac{G(w)}{G(0)^{1/2}}, \tag{49.7}$$

and call $f(z)$ and $g(w)$ the *reduced theta products*. Then 49.6 takes the simpler form

$$u_1(z+w)\,u_2(z-w) = f(z)\,f(w) \pm g(z)\,g(w). \qquad (49.8)$$

Since $u_1(z-w)\,u_2(z+w)$ and $u_1(z+w)\,u_2(z-w)$ are both solutions of 49.3, their sums and differences must also be solutions. Hence the functions $f(z)f(w)$ and $g(z)g(w)$ must also be solutions of the same equation.

We thus have the relation

$$\frac{\partial^2}{\partial z^2}\,[f(z)\,f(w)] + \frac{\partial^2}{\partial w^2}\,[f(z)\,f(w)] = -\frac{8}{\pi i}\,\frac{\partial}{\partial t}\,[f(z)\,f(w)] \qquad (49.9)$$

for all z and w. From this it follows that

$$\frac{\partial^2 f(z)}{\partial z^2} + \frac{8}{\pi i}\cdot\frac{\partial f(z)}{\partial t} = kf(z),$$

$$\frac{\partial^2 f(w)}{\partial w^2} + \frac{8}{\pi i}\cdot\frac{\partial f(w)}{\partial t} = -kf(w), \qquad (49.10)$$

where k is independent of both z and w, and thus must be identically zero.

It follows that the reduced theta products satisfy the simple partial differential equation

$$\frac{\partial^2 U}{\partial z^2} = -\frac{8}{\pi i}\,\frac{\partial u}{\partial t}. \qquad (49.11)$$

Some further results may be found in Schottky's note.

Comments and References

See

Schottky, F., "Einige Folgerungen aus bekannten Thetaformeln." *S. B. preuss. Akad. Wiss.*, **XXX** (1927) 215.

For a different application of differential equations, see

Van der Pol, B., "On a nonlinear partial differential equation satisfied by the logarithm of the Jacobian theta-functions, with applications, I, II." *Proc. Acad. Sci. Amst. (A)*, **13** (1951) 261; 272.

50. Functional Equations

We now wish to introduce a technique which is quite different from any of those employed in the previous pages, a technique based purely upon functional equations. Not only can this procedure be used to derive many of the results so far obtained, but it also serves to motivate them and explain their origin.

Furthermore, it can be used in precisely analogous fashion to explore the domain of multidimensional theta functions. This is a matter of some importance, since the multidimensional theta functions—functions of several complex variables which we shall meet in a moment—are not so susceptible to the power of the theory of functions of a complex variable as the one-dimensional functions so far encountered.

The basic idea we exploit is that the functional equations of Section 3 completely determine the theta functions, up to multiplicative constants. This observation, together with some elementary manipulations, suffices to determine the fundamental properties of the theta functions.

Comments and References

Although functional equations have been used in similar fashion by various authors, such as the papers by Basoco and Mordell cited above, and

Estermann, T., "On the representation of a number as a sum of squares." *Proc. Lond. math. Soc.*, **9** (1959) 574, Theorem 4,

the systematic use of this technique given below to handle theta functions of one variable appears to be new. See

Bellman, R., "Functional equations and theta-functions—I." *Proc. nat. Acad. Sci.* Washington, D. C., **45** (1959) 853.

It is possible that the multidimensional generalizations of the Cauchy residue theorem, due to Poincaré, and foreshadowed by some algebraic results of Jacobi, may play an important role in the theory of multidimensional theta functions, but so far nothing has been done in this direction. See

Jacobi, C. G., "Theoremeta nova algebraica circa systema duarum aequationum inter duas variables propasitorum." *Œuvres*, **3**, pp. 287-294.

and Chapter VI of

Forsyth, A. R., *Theory of Functions of Two Complex Variables*. Cambridge: Cambridge Univ. Press, 1914.

This method is used in

Baker, H. F., *Multiply-periodic functions*. Cambridge: Cambridge Univ. Press, 1907.

to treat theta functions of several variables; see also

Riemann, B., *Collected Works of Bernhard Riemann*. New York: Dover Publ. Co., 1953, p. 128, "Theorie der Abelschen Functionen".

51. Determination of Theta Functions

Consider the pair of functional equations

(a) $f(z + \pi) = f(z)$,

(b) $f(z + \pi t) = b e^{-2iz} f(z)$,   (51.1) where b is at the moment an unspecified constant, independent of z, but possibly dependent on t. Suppose initially that we are interested only in solutions which are analytic functions of z throughout the entire finite z plane—that is, entire, and which, in addition, possess absolutely convergent Fourier expansions of the form

$$f(z) = \sum_{n=-\infty}^{\infty} c_n e^{2niz}, \qquad (51.2)$$

for all finite z.

As we shall see below, the second assumption is a consequence of the first and the periodicity of $f(z)$.

Substituting the Fourier series expansion of 51.2 into 51.1 (b) and equating coefficients, we obtain the recurrence relation

$$c_{n+1} = b^{-1} q^{2n} c_n, \qquad (51.3)$$

connecting successive coefficients. Iterating this relation, it follows that

$$c_n = b^{-n} q^{2(n-1)+2(n-2)+\cdots+2} c_0,$$
$$= b^{-n} q^{n(n-1)} c_0, \qquad (51.4)$$

for $n > 0$, and it is readily verified that the same formula holds also for $n < 0$.

We then have the following expression for $f(z)$,

$$f(z) = c_0 \left[1 + \sum_{n=-\infty}^{\infty} q^{n(n-1)} b^{-n} e^{2niz} \right]. \qquad (51.5)$$

If we suppose that $|q| = |e^{\pi i t}| < 1$, which is to say $Im(t) > 0$, this series converges for all finite z and actually represents an entire function of z. It follows that any function possessing such a Fourier series is uniquely determined, up to a multiplicative constant, by the pair of equation in 51.1.

Taking the particular choice $b = -q^{-1}$, we obtain the function $\theta_3(z)$.

52. Entire Solutions

Let us now show that it is sufficient to assume that the function $f(z)$ for which we are looking is entire. It turns out that the periodicity condition automatically guarantees that it possesses a Fourier expansion which is convergent throughout the finite z plane.

To establish this, consider the integral

$$\int_C f(z) e^{-2niz} \, dz = 0, \qquad (52.1)$$

where C consists of a rectangle whose corners are at the points $-\pi/2$, $\pi/2$, $-\pi/2 - ik$, $\pi/2 - ik$. The equation in 52.1 is equivalent to the relation

$$\int_{-\pi/2}^{\pi/2} f(z)\, e^{-2inz}\, dz + \int_{\pi/2}^{\pi/2-ik} + \int_{\pi/2+ik}^{-\pi/2-ik} + \int_{-\pi/2-ik}^{-\pi/2} = 0. \qquad (52.2)$$

The second and fourth integrals cancel, because of the periodicity of the function $f(z)$. Hence,

$$\int_{-\pi/2}^{\pi/2} f(z)\, e^{-2inz}\, dz = \int_{-\pi/2-ik}^{\pi/2-ik} f(z)\, e^{-2inz}\, dz$$

$$= \int_{-\pi/2}^{\pi/2} f(w - ik)\, e^{-2ni(w-ik)}\, dw$$

$$= e^{-2kn} \int_{-\pi/2}^{\pi/2} f(w - ik)\, e^{-2niw}\, dw. \qquad (52.3)$$

From this follows the inequality

$$\left| \int_{-\pi/2}^{\pi/2} f(z)\, e^{-2inz}\, dz \right| \le e^{-2kn}\pi \max_{-\pi/2 \le w \le \pi/2} | f(w - ik)\, |. \qquad (52.4)$$

Let us take k and n positive. It follows that the Fourier coefficients with positive indices are $0\,(e^{-2kn})$ for any positive k, where, of course, the constant implied by 0 is dependent upon k, but not upon n. Reversing the sign of k, we obtain a similar estimate for negative n.

Since k can be chosen arbitrarily, it follows that the function $f(z)$, and hence $f(z + \pi t)$, possesses an absolutely convergent Fourier expansion for all finite z. From this, we deduce that the method of equating coefficients used in the foregoing section is valid.

53. Hermite's Method

Alternatively, we now consider the integral

$$\int_C f(z)\, e^{-2niz}\, dz = 0 \qquad (53.1)$$

taken around the rectangle whose corners are $-\pi/2$, $\pi/2$, $-\pi/2 + \pi t$, $\pi/2 + \pi t$, and readily derive the recurrence relations of 51.3 upon using the functional equations of 51.1.

54. Statement of Result

We have thus established

Theorem 10: *If $Im(t) > 0$, every entire solution of*

$$f(z + \pi) = f(z),$$
$$f(z + \pi t) = be^{-2iz} f(z), \qquad (54.1)$$

is a constant multiple of the function

$$f(z) = 1 + \sum_{n=-\infty}^{\infty} q^{n^2-n} b^{-n} e^{2niz}. \tag{54.2}$$

As noted above, if we choose $q = b^{-1}$, we obtain the theta function $\theta_3(z)$. With this result as a basis, we are now ready to furnish some alternative proofs to the results of the preceding sections.

55. Fundamental Transformation Formula

We can now establish the fundamental transformation formula

$$\theta_3(z, t) = (-it)^{-1/2} e^{z^2\pi/it} \theta_3\left(\frac{z}{t}, -\frac{1}{t}\right), \tag{55.1}$$

using the uniqueness result contained in theorem 10. Consider the function

$$f(z) = e^{z^2/\pi it} \theta_3\left(\frac{z}{t}, -\frac{1}{t}\right). \tag{55.2}$$

We have

$$f(z + \pi) = e^{(z^2+2z\pi+\pi^2)/\pi it} \theta_3\left(\frac{z}{t} + \frac{\pi}{t}, -\frac{1}{t}\right). \tag{55.3}$$

Since

$$\theta_3\left(\frac{z}{t} + \pi, -\frac{1}{t}\right) = e^{-\pi i/t} e^{2iz/t} \theta_3\left(\frac{z}{t}, -\frac{1}{t}\right), \tag{55.4}$$

we see that $f(z)$, despite its unlikely appearance, is actually periodic of period π,

$$f(z + \pi) = f(z). \tag{55.5}$$

Similarly, it is easy to verify that

$$f(z + \pi t) = q^{-1} e^{-2iz} f(z). \tag{55.6}$$

It follows from the basic uniqueness theorem of Section 54 that $f(z)$ must be a constant multiple of $\theta_3(z, t)$, which is to say

$$\theta_3(z, t) = g(t) e^{z^2/\pi it} \theta_3\left(\frac{z}{t}, -\frac{1}{t}\right), \tag{55.7}$$

where $g(t)$ depends only upon t and not upon z. In the next section, we shall turn to the determination of this parameter.

56. Determination of $g(t)$

There are several ways of determining the function $g(t)$. The simplest, perhaps, is the following. Choose $z = 0$, obtaining the relation

$$e^{-z^2/\pi it} \frac{\theta_3(z, t)}{\theta_3(z/t, -1/t)} = \frac{\theta_3(0, t)}{\theta_3(0, -1/t)} = g(t). \tag{56.1}$$

It follows that the general modular transformation is made to depend upon the special case where $z = 0$. This special relation can be established in many different ways, as we have seen.

A second way is to normalize the solution $\theta_3(z,t)$ by the requirement that it satisfy the equation

$$\frac{\partial u}{\partial t} = \frac{\pi}{4i} \frac{\partial^2 u}{\partial z^2}. \tag{56.2}$$

This yields the desired result

$$g(t) = (-it)^{-1/2}. \tag{56.3}$$

Comments and References

For further discussions and extensions, see

Bellman, R., and Lehman, S., "The Reciprocity Formula for Multi-dimensional Theta-Functions" (to appear).

57. The infinite Product

In Section 34 we considered the infinite product

$$f(z) = \prod_{n=1}^{\infty} (1 - 2q^{2n-1} \cos z + q^{4n-2}) \tag{57.1}$$

and established directly that it satisfies the functional equations of 54.1. Since the infinite product is readily seen to be an entire function of z, we have an alternative proof of the result of 32.2. We still face in any of these procedures the difficult task of determining the function $g(t)$ (see the discussion at the end of Section 32).

58. Linear Space of Solutions

Precisely the same type of analysis pursued above enables us to assert

Theorem 11: *Any entire solution of the system of equations*

$$f(z + \pi) = f(z),$$
$$f(z + \pi t) = be^{-2kiz} f(z) \tag{58.1}$$

where $Im(t) > 0$ and k is a positive integer, is a linear combination of k particular solutions.

In other words, the set of solutions of the functional equations of 58.1 constitutes a k dimensional linear manifold.

59.   Relations Connecting Squares

Many of the relations demonstrated in Section 45-48 now become rather easy to understand. To begin with, let us examine the relation connecting squares of theta functions. Consider the four possible functional equations

$$\theta(z + \pi) = \pm\, \theta(z),$$

$$\theta(z + \pi t) = \pm\, q^{-1} e^{-2iz}\, \theta(z) \tag{59.1}$$

satisfied by the four theta functions. Squaring each of these equations, we have the two equations

$$u(z + \pi) = u(z),$$

$$u(z + \pi t) = q^{-2} e^{-4iz}\, u(z), \tag{59.2}$$

satisfied by the square of any of the four theta functions. By virtue of the foregoing theorem, there must be a linear relation connecting any set of three different squares.

60.   Addition Formula

Consider the functional equations satisfied by $\theta(z + y)$,

$$\theta(z + y + \pi) = \pm\, \theta(z + y),$$

$$\theta(z + y + \pi t) = \pm\, q^{-1}\, e^{-2i(z+y)}\, \theta(z + y). \tag{60.1}$$

It follows that the function

$$g(z) = \theta_i(z + y)\, \theta_j(z - y) \tag{60.2}$$

satisfies the functional equations

$$g(z + \pi) = g(z),$$

$$g(z + \pi t) = q^{-2} e^{-4iz}\, g(z), \tag{60.3}$$

provided that $\theta_i(z)$ and $\theta_j(z)$ are associated with the proper combinations of $+$'s and $-$'s.

The relation of Section 46 is now clear.

Comments and References

The reader who is interested in pursuing the subject may verify that the more complex results of Jacobi pertaining to theta functions whose arguments are linear combinations of z_1, z_2, z_3, and z_4 may be derived in the same way. It is easy to see that many more identities of this nature can be obtained along the same lines.

61.　Multidimensional Theta Functions

Theta functions of one complex variable are, as we have already mentioned here and there, the building blocks of elliptic functions, and thus are intimately related to elliptic integrals, such as

$$\int \frac{dx}{[(1 - x^2)(1 - k^2 x^2)]^{1/2}} \, . \tag{61.1}$$

Jacobi was the first to indicate how to connect theta functions of several complex variables to general algebraic integrals of the form

$$\int R(x, y) \, dx \tag{61.2}$$

where R is a rational function and x and y are connected by a polynomial relation of the form $P(x, y) = 0$.

The development of this theme was one of the major enterprises of nineteenth century mathematics, with an enormous influence upon contemporary developments.

The general form of a theta function of several complex variables, $z_1, z_2, ..., z_N$ is

$$\theta(z_1, z_2, ..., z_N) = \sum_{n_j} \left[\exp \left(2\pi i \sum_{j=1}^{N} z_j n_j - \sum_{i,j=1}^{N} t_{ij} n_i n_j \right) \right] . \tag{61.3}$$

where the summation is over all possible sets of positive and negative integers and zero for the n_j. As we shall briefly sketch below, these functions possess many of the properties of the one-dimensional functions. Many further results will be found in references we shall furnish.

62.　Vector-matrix Notation

The easiest way to spotlight the similarities is to introduce a less cumbersome notation. Let us then employ some elementary vector-matrix notation. Set

$$z = \begin{pmatrix} z_1 \\ z_2 \\ \vdots \\ z_N \end{pmatrix} , \qquad n = \begin{pmatrix} n_1 \\ n_2 \\ \vdots \\ n_N \end{pmatrix} , \qquad T = (t_{ij}), \qquad i, j = 1, 2, ..., N. \tag{62.1}$$

The components of the column vector z are complex variables, while those of n are positive or negative integers or zero; the elements of T, a square matrix, are complex variables. If we employ the inner product notation

$$(z, w) = \sum_{i=1}^{N} z_i w_i \tag{62.2}$$

we may write, quite compactly,

$$\theta(z, T) = \theta(z) = \sum_n e^{2\pi i(n, z) - (n, Tn)}. \tag{62.3}$$

Comments and References

The reader wishing further information concerning vectors and matrices, and discussion of some of the results we employ below, may consult

Bellman, R., *Introduction to Matrix Analysis*. New York: McGraw-Hill Book Co., Inc., 1960.

63. Convergence Proof

Let us now show that $\theta(z,T)$ is an entire function of z, which is to say of the components of z, provided that T is a symmetric matrix whose real part is positive definite. By this we mean that T has the form $T_1 + iT_2$, where T_1 and T_2 are both real and symmetric and

$$(x, T_1 x) \geq \lambda_1(x, x), \qquad \lambda_1 > 0, \tag{63.1}$$

for *all* real vectors x. If this condition holds, it is easily seen that the series for $\theta(z, T)$ is majorized by the series

$$\left(\sum_{n_1 = -\infty}^{\infty} e^{2\pi |n_1| a_1 - n_1^2 \lambda_1} \right)^N, \qquad a_1 = \max(|z_1|, |z_2|, ..., |z_N|). \tag{63.2}$$

It follows that the series for $\theta(z, T)$ is absolutely and uniformly convergent for all finite z and thus represents an entire function of z.

64. Elementary Functional Relations

Let e_k denote a unit vector

$$e_k = \begin{bmatrix} 0 \\ \vdots \\ 1 \\ \vdots \\ 0 \end{bmatrix}, \tag{64.1}$$

where all of the components are zero except for a 1 which occurs in the kth place. Then

$$\theta(z, T) = \sum_{n}' e^{2\pi i(n+e_k, z) - (n+e_k, Tn + Te_k)}$$

$$= e^{2\pi i(e_k, z) - (e_k, Te_k)} \sum_{n}' e^{2\pi i(n, z) - (n, Tn) - 2(n, Te_k)}$$

$$= e^{2\pi i(e_k, z) - (e_k, Te_k)} \sum_{n}' e^{2\pi i(n, z + iTe_k) - (n, Tn)}$$

$$= e^{2\pi i(e_k, z) - (e_k, Te_k)} \theta(z + iTe_k, T).$$

Hence the fundamental elementary relations satisfied by the multidimensional theta functions are

$$\theta(z + e_k, T) = \theta(z, T), \qquad k = 1, 2, ..., N, \tag{64.3}$$

periodicity in each component, and

$$\theta(z + iTe_k, T) = e^{-2\pi i(e_k, z) + (e_k, Te_k)} \theta(z, T). \tag{64.4}$$

As might be expected, these relations determine the function, up to a multiplicative constant.

65. Multidimensional Fourier Series

To obtain the analogue of the modular transformation for functions of one complex variable, we shall use multidimensional Fourier series. We shall proceed in a formal manner with the comment that it is not difficult to justify our procedures for the class of functions with which we are dealing.

If $f(x) = f(x_1, x_2, ..., x_N)$ is a function which is periodic of period one in each of its components, we expand it in a multiple Fourier series

$$f(x) = \sum a_{n_1 n_2 \cdots n_N} e^{2\pi i(n_1 x_1 + n_2 x_2 + \cdots + n_N x_N)}$$

$$= \sum a_n e^{2\pi i(n, x)}. \tag{65.1}$$

Then, as in the one-dimensional case, the coefficients are determined by the relation

$$a_n = \int_0^1 \cdots \int_0^1 f(y) e^{-2\pi i(n, y)} dy_1 dy_2 ... dy_N. \tag{65.2}$$

or, in our shorthand notation,

$$a_n = \int_0^1 f(y) e^{-2\pi i(n, y)} dy. \tag{65.3}$$

66. Multidimensional Poisson Summation Formula

Let $g(x) = g(x_1, x_2, \dots x_N)$ be a function defined over the entire x plane, suitably behaved at infinity so that the following infinite series exists,

$$f(x) = \sum_n g(x + n). \tag{66.1}$$

The function $f(x)$ is then a periodic function of period one in all of the components of x. Expanding it in a Fourier series, pursuant to Hecke's dictum, we have

$$f(x) = \sum_n a_n e^{2\pi i(n, x)}, \tag{66.2}$$

where

$$
\begin{aligned}
a_n &= \int_0^1 f(y)\, e^{-2\pi i(n, y)}\, dy \\
&= \int_0^1 \left[\sum_m g(y + m) \right] e^{-2\pi i(n, y)}\, dy \\
&= \sum_m \int_{R_m} g(y)\, e^{-2\pi i(n, y)}\, dy \\
&= \int_{-\infty}^{\infty} g(y)\, e^{-2\pi i(n, y)}\, dy.
\end{aligned}
\tag{66.3}
$$

Hence, purely formally, we have the multidimensional Poisson summation formula

$$\sum_m g(x + m) = \sum_n e^{2\pi i(n, x)} \left[\int_{-\infty}^{\infty} g(y)\, e^{-2\pi i(n, y)}\, dy \right]. \tag{66.4}$$

The case $x = 0$ is of particular interest

$$\sum_m g(m) = \sum_n \left[\int_{-\infty}^{\infty} g(y) e^{-2\pi i(n, y)}\, dy \right]. \tag{66.5}$$

We shall use this form below.

Comments and References

Taking $g(x)$ to have a particular structural form, a number of very elegant results can be obtained. Thus we can take $g(x)$ to have the form $g(x_1^2 + x_2^2 + \dots + x_N^2)$, $g(x_1 x_2 \dots x_N)$, or $g(x_1^2 - x_2^2 - \dots - x_N^2)$, or, as a function of the variables x_{ij} $N \geq j \geq i \geq 1$, to have the form $g(|\, x_{ij}\, |)$ where $|\, x_{ij}\, |$ represents the determinant of the square matrix $X = (x_{ij})$. For examples of what can be obtained in this way, see

Bellman, R., "A generalization of some integral identities due to Ingham and Siegel." *Duke math. J.*, **24** (1956) 571.

Bochner, S., *Vorlesungen über die Fouriersche Integrale*. Leipzig: 1932.

────── "Group invariance of Cauchy's formula in several variables." *Ann. Math.*, **45** (1944) 686.

Mordell, L. J., "Some applications of a transformation of series." *Proc. Lond. Math. Soc.*, **27** (1928), pp. 81-104.

──────"Poisson's summation formula in several variables and some applications to the theory of numbers," *Proc. Camb. Phil. Soc.*, **25** (1929).

────── "Hecke's modular functions and other analytic functions in the theory of numbers," *Proc. Lond. Math. Soc.*, **32** (1930).

Siegel, C. L., "Über die analytische Theorie der quadratischen Formen." *Ann. Math.*, **36** (1935) 527.

67. An Infinite Integral

In order to apply the Poisson summation to the study of multidimensional theta functions, we must evaluate the infinite integral

$$J_n = \int_{-\infty}^{\infty} \exp\left[-(y, Ty) - 2\pi i(n, y)\right] dy$$

$$= \int_{-\infty}^{\infty} \cdots \int_{-\infty}^{\infty} \exp\left(-\sum_{i,j=1}^{N} t_{ij} y_i y_j - 2\pi i \sum_{j=1}^{N} n_j y_j\right) dy_1\, dy_2 \ldots dy_N. \qquad (67.1)$$

We shall accomplish this by considering first the more general integral

$$J(x) = \int_{-\infty}^{\infty} e^{-(y, Ty) - 2(x, y)}\, dy \qquad (67.2)$$

under the assumption that x is a real vector and that T is a positive definite symmetric matrix. Since the integral is an analytic function of x for all x provided that T is a matrix whose real part is positive definite, and an analytic function of T in this region of the t_{ij} space, any analytic representation we obtain for real x and real T will be valid in the wider domain. There are, of course, direct ways of evaluating $J(x)$, but the appeal to analytic continuation is certainly the easiest.

Using the identity

$$[y + T^{-1}x, T(y + T^{-1}x)] = (y, Ty) + 2(y, Tx) + (x, T^{-1}x), \qquad (67.3)$$

where T^{-1} is the inverse of T, we see that

$$J(x) = e^{(x, T^{-1}x)} \int_{-\infty}^{\infty} e^{-[y+T^{-1}x, T(y+T^{-1}x)]}\, dy. \qquad (67.4)$$

Hence a change of variable yields the partial result

$$J(x) = e^{(x, T^{-1}x)} \int_{-\infty}^{\infty} e^{-(y, Ty)}\, dy. \qquad (67.5)$$

It is clear that the right-hand side is an analytic function of x and T for all x, provided that the real part of T is positive definite. Hence this representation, established initially only for real x and real T which are positive definite, holds in the wider domain.

68. Evaluation of $\int_{-\infty}^{\infty} e^{-(y, Ty)} \, dy$

The infinite integral

$$I = \int_{-\infty}^{\infty} e^{-(y, Ty)} \, dy \tag{68.1}$$

can be evaluated in a number of ways. As above, let us begin with the case where T is a real positive definite matrix. The simplest method uses the canonical form of a positive definite matrix. Let S be an orthogonal matrix with the property that

$$S'TS = \begin{pmatrix} \lambda_1 & & & 0 \\ & \lambda_2 & & \\ & & \ddots & \\ 0 & & & \lambda_N \end{pmatrix} \tag{68.2}$$

where the λ_i, the characteristic roots of T, are positive since T is by assumption positive definite. Here, S' denotes the transpose of S.

The change of variable $y = Sz$, which has Jacobian equal to one, leads to the relation

$$I = \int_{-\infty}^{\infty} e^{-(Sz, TSz)} \, dz = \int_{-\infty}^{\infty} e^{-(z, S'TSz)} \, dz$$

$$= \int_{-\infty}^{\infty} \cdots \int_{-\infty}^{\infty} e^{-(\lambda_1 z_1^2 + \lambda_2 z_2^2 + \cdots + \lambda_N z_N^2)} \, dz_1 \, dz_2 \, \ldots \, dz_N$$

$$= \left(\int_{-\infty}^{\infty} e^{-\lambda_1 z_1^2} \, dz_1 \right) \cdots \left(\int_{-\infty}^{\infty} e^{-\lambda_N z_N^2} \, dz_N \right)$$

$$= \frac{\pi^{N/2}}{(\lambda_1 \lambda_2 \ldots \lambda_N)^{1/2}} . \tag{68.3}$$

Since the product of the characteristic roots, is equal to $|T|$, the determinant of T, we obtain the desired result

$$\int_{-\infty}^{\infty} e^{-(y, Ty)} \, dy = \frac{\pi^{N/2}}{|T|^{1/2}} \tag{68.4}$$

valid for positive definite T. Analytic continuation now assures us that this is valid for all symmetric T which have positive definite real parts, provided that we use the principal value of the square root.

Comments and References

The matrix theory required for the foregoing derivation can be found in the book by R. Bellman cited above. On page 97 of this book will be found another derivation which can be used to obtain some deeper results. See

Bellman, R., "A generalization of some integral identities due to Ingham and Siegel." *Duke math. J.*, **24** (1956) 571.

Olkin, I., "A class of integral identities with matrix argument." *Duke math. J.*, **26** (1959) 207.

69.   The Modular Transformation

Turning back to the relation of 66.5, we have

$$\sum_n e^{-(n,\,Tn)+2\pi i(n,\,z)} = \sum_n \left[\int_{-\infty}^{\infty} e^{-(y,\,Ty)+2\pi i(y,\,z)-2\pi i(n,\,y)}\ dy \right]$$

$$= \sum_n \int_{-\infty}^{\infty} e^{-(y,\,Ty)+2(y,\,\pi i z+\pi i n)}\ dy$$

$$= \sum_n \frac{\pi^{N/2}}{\mid T \mid^{1/2}}\, e^{[\pi i z+\pi i n,\,T^{-1}(\pi i z+\pi i n)]}$$

$$= \frac{\pi^{N/2}}{\mid T \mid^{1/2}} \sum_n e^{-\pi^2[z+n,\,T^{-1}(z+n)]}. \tag{69.1}$$

We thus obtain the fundamental transformation formula

$$\sum_n e^{-(n,\,Tn)+2\pi i(n,\,z)} = \frac{\pi^{N/2}}{\mid T \mid^{1/2}} \sum_n e^{-\pi^2[z+n,\,T^{-1}(z+n)]} \tag{69.2}$$

valid for all z, and for all T with real part positive definite.

Theorem 9.

$$\theta\,(z,\,T) = \frac{\pi^{N/2}}{\mid T \mid^{1/2}}\,\theta\,(T^{-1}\,z,\,T^{-1})\,. \tag{69.3}$$

Comments and References

For a systematic development of the theory of multi-dimensional theta functions, see

Baker, H. F., *An Introduction to the Theory of Multiply Periodic Functions*. Cambridge: Cambridge Univ. Press, 1907.

Many other references will be found there. Also see

Forsyth, A. R., *Theory of Functions of Two Complex Variables*. Cambridge: Cambridge Univ. Press, 1914.

For an inductive proof of the multidimensional transformation formula, starting with the one-dimensional case, see pages 62-63 of the book by Landau referred to below.

70. Generalizations and Particularizations

Perhaps the principal difficulty in the theory of multidimensional theta functions lies in the fact that there are too many of them. In attempts to single out those of paramount significance, Hecke and Siegel, influenced by some ideas of Hilbert, have introduced theta functions closely associated with algebraic numbers and with matrices. Since any discussion of these matters would take us quite far afield and demand of the reader far more than we have so far needed, we shall merely refer to the following sources. For the papers of Hecke, perhaps the most easily accessible reference is his collected works.

Comments and References

Hecke, E., *Mathematische Werke.* Göttingen: Vordenhoeck und Ruprecht, 1959.

Hecke, E., *Dirichlet Series, Modular Functions and Quadratic Forms.* Princeton : The Institute for Advanced Study, 1938.

See also

Götzky, F., "Über eine zahlentheoretische Anwendung von Modulfunktionen zweier Veränderlichen." *Math. Ann.,* **100** (1928) 411.
Kloosterman, H. D., "Thetareihen in total-reelen algebraischen Zahlkörpern." *Math. Ann.,* **103** (1930) 279.
Mordell, L. J., "On Hecke's modular functions, zeta functions, and some other analytic functions in the theory of numbers," *Proc. Lond. Math. Soc.,* **32** (1930-1), 501.

For an introduction to the generalized theta functions of Siegel, see

Siegel, C. L., "Über die analytische Theorie der quadratischen Formen." *Ann. Math.,* **36** (1935) 527.

Nonanalytic functions possessing modular transformations were introduced by Maass,

Maass, H., "Über eine neue Art von nonanalytischen automorphen Funktionen und die Bestimmung Dirichletschen Reihen durch Funktionalgleichungen." *Math. Ann.,* **121** (1949) 141.

and subsequently generalized by Siegel,

Siegel, C. L., "Indefinite quadratische Formen und Funktionentheorie, I." *Math. Ann.,* **124** (1951) 17; "II," 364.

See also

Bellman, R., "Generalized Eisenstein series and non-analytic automorphic functions." *Proc. nat. Acad. Sci.,* Wash., **36** (1950) 356.

The generalized theta functions give rise to associated generalized zeta functions with functional equations similar to those of the Riemann zeta function; see

Bellman, R., "On the functional equations of the Dirichlet series derived from Siegel modular forms." *Proc. nat. Acad. Sci.*, Wash., **37** (1951) 84.
————, "A generalization of some integral identities due to Ingham and Siegel." *Duke math. J.*, **24** (1956) 571.
Maass, H., "Modulformen zweiten Grade und Dirichletreihen." *Math. Ann.*, **122** (1950) 90.

For the application of the multidimensional theta functions to ideal theory, see

Landau, E., *Algebraischen Zahlen und der Ideale*. New York: Chelsea Publ. Co., 1948.
Hecke, E., *Algebraischen Zahlen*, New York: Chelsea Publ. Co., 1948.

Indexes

Subject

Author

Subject Index

analytic paraphrase, 20
approximate functional equation, 53
approximations, 11
arithmetic-geometric mean, 55
automorphic functions, 13-15

basic hypergeometric series, 47-49
Bessel function, 23, 26-27
binomial expansion, 40-41

circle method, 14-15
cyclotomic sums, 40

diffusion, 41
diffusion equation, 13
Dirichlet divisor function, 37
Dirichlet divisor problem, 23
Dirichlet series, 28, 36-37
duplication formula, 30

Eisenstein series, 12, 71
Euler factorization, 33
Eulerian results, 47-48

fake theta functions, 52
formulae
    duplication, 30
    inversion, 28
    Poisson summation, 6-7, 9, 34, 36, 67, 68
    summation, 36, 37
    transformation, 10-11
Fourier expansion, 45
Fourier series, 4-7
functional equation, 32, 33, 39
functions
    automorphic, 13-15
    Bessel, 23, 26-27
    Dirichlet divisor, 37
    fake theta, 52
    gamma, 30
    Gauss circle, 37
    mock theta, 48, 51-52

modular, 12, 68, 71
multidimensional theta, 64, 70, 72
Riemann zeta, 30-32
theta, 1-3
zeta, 34-36
fundamental domain, 3-4

gamma function, 30
Gauss circle function, 37
Gauss sum, 38, 50, 52

heat equation, 16
hypergeometric series, 48

infinite integral, 68, 69
infinite product, 43, 51, 62
integral identities, 69
inversion formula, 28

Landen transformation, 55
Laplace transform, 20
lattice points, 16
lemniscate, 40
Liouville's theorem, 1, 44, 46

Mellin transform, 28-31
mock theta functions, 48, 51-52
modular functions, 12, 68, 71
modular transformation, 70, 71
Mordell integral, 52-53
multidimensional Fourier series, 66
multidimensional Poisson summation formula, 67
multidimensional theta functions, 64, 70, 72

partial fractions, 50-51
Poisson summation formula, 6-7, 9, 34, 36, 67, 68

random walk, 41
Riemann hypothesis, 33-34
Riemann zeta function, 30-32

75

Author Index

77